Looking to the Future

Looking to the Future

Key Issues for Contemporary Mental Health Services

Edited by Thurstine Basset

© Pavilion Publishing/Mental Health Foundation

The authors have asserted their rights in accordance with the *Copyright, Designs and Patents Act 1988* to be identified as the authors of this work.

Published by:

Pavilion Publishing (Brighton) Ltd
The Ironworks
Cheapside
Brighton
East Sussex
BN1 4GD

Tel: 01273 623222
Fax: 01273 625526
Email: info@pavpub.com
Web: www.pavpub.com

In association with:
Mental Health Foundation
20-21 Cornwall Terrace
London
NW1 4QL

First published 2000. Reprinted 2001 (twice).

A catalogue record for this book is available from the British Library.

ISBN 1 84196 031 4

Pavilion editor: Jo Hathaway
Pavilion designer: Greg Levitt
Printing by: Ashford Press (Southampton)

Looking to the Future

Key issues for contemporary mental
health services

Contents

Ways of Working

To illustrate the text, Contact have provided a series of
photographs which appear throughout the book. These are
listed below:

David Arnold
I'm Not Well 1
I'm Not Well 2

Leila Atherton
Holding On To Peace and Tranquility, An Escape
New Sussex Hospital

Olive M.
From the series "Millview Hospital" Millview Garden:
Hope for the Future
From the series "New Sussex Hospital" Trap Door:
What can it be, this mystery? A square amidst conformity

Pierre M.
From the series "In Sanity": Deteriorating Faculties
From the series "In Sanity": Tranquility of Mind

Chrissy S.
Sleepless Nights 1
Sleepless Nights 2

Mike Smith
Treatment? 1
Treatment? 2

Jack Scivyer
Don't Lose Your Head 1
Don't Lose Your Head 2

Jeremy Wooldridge
Arrive in Time
Release

Acknowledgements

Editor: Thurstine Basset

Thanks to group members of Contact, Magali Nougarede and Lorna Jones for the photographs and accompanying text.

Looking to the Future is a reader produced to accompany the Certificate in Community Mental Health Care. Various people and organisations have been involved in work related to the Certificate, as listed below.

Project team for the Certificate in Community Mental Health Care

Mental Health Foundation: Nigel Duerdoth, Alison Clare, Thurstine Basset and Sarah Wright.

City & Guilds Affinity: Peter Mathias, Jackie Richards and members of the Affinity Team.

City & Guilds: Chahid Fourali, Sarah Austin and Lorna Mullard.

Pavilion Publishing: Edwina Rowling, Loretta Harrison and Jo Hathaway.

TOPSS representative: Pam Blackman

Project director: Alison Clare

Materials co-ordinator and writer: Thurstine Basset

Writer of Units 8 and 9: Sharon Cuthbert

Writer of Guidance to the Certificate: Alison Clare

City & Guilds Affinity Outcomes and Assessment Group: Chahid Fourali, Katie Glover, Jo Borrill, Jan Wallcraft, Carol Magnus, Margaret Pedler, Valerie McLeod, Sharon Cuthbert, Alison Murray, Malcolm Phillips, David Pilgrim, Suman Fernando and Peter Campbell.

Thanks to the members of the **Mental Health Foundation's Advisory Committee** who helped to steer the Certificate through its various stages.

Thanks also to Cliff Prior (now with NSF) and Dawn Wakeling (now with Mind) who were responsible for initiating the plans for the Certificate when they worked for the Mental Health Foundation.

Co-ordinators, trainers and tutors on seven pilot sites for the Certificate:

Belfast: Maria Lowry and Lorraine Girvan.

Birmingham: Jo Glover, Teresa Moran, Tina Braithwaite and Guy Wishart.

Blackburn: David Dixon, David Pilgrim and Mandee Leese.

Edinburgh: Wendy Spencer, Angela Benicki and Norman Lyon.

Gwynedd: David Reader and Barbara Howell.

London: Ann-Marie Spence, Katie Glover, Matthew House, Stuart Hannell, Frank Kiyimba, Soo Moore, Emer O'Neill and Michael Phelan.

Suffolk: Carol Magnus, Dan Dziobon, Chris Sharpe and Ian Hartley.

Thanks to the students who participated in the pilots and whose feedback has enhanced the contents of this book.

Contributors

Su Akbar-Khan is a community psychiatric nurse and works for IMPACT - Hammersmith & Fulham Mind.

Frank Bangay is a survivor of the psychiatric system. He has been writing poetry since 1972. Some of the poems in this book are taken from his book, *Naked Songs and Rhythms of Hope* which was published in 1999 by Forreal Editions.

Jo Borrill is Clinical Research Manager at the Mental Health Foundation, and is responsible for external academic research programmes on various subjects, including psychotherapy, schizophrenia and dementia research.

Alison Faulkner is Project Manager of the Strategies for Living project at the Mental Health Foundation.

Loretta Fuller is presently working as the Outreach and Community Support Manager at the Frantz Fanon Centre for Mental Health, Birmingham.

Mo Hutchison is a freelance user consultant. She also works as Senior User Consultant to the Centre for Mental Health Services Development at King's College, London

Maria Lowry is Operations Manager for National Schizophrenia Fellowship in Northern Ireland.

Steve Morgan is a Practice Development Manager for Risk at the Sainsbury Centre for Mental Health.

Roger Moss is a retired consultant psychiatrist from South Devon. He was formerly Senior Psychiatric Adviser at the Centre for Mental Health Services Development at King's College, London.

Alison Murray is an independent research psychologist and Research Fellow at St. Bartholomew's and the Royal London School of Medicine and Dentristry.

Steve Onyett is Head of Psychology in Adult Mental Health for Severn NHS Trust, and a consultant/trainer at The Sainsbury Centre for Mental Health.

Margaret Pedler is Head of Policy Development for Mind.

David Pilgrim is Head of Adult and Forensic Clinical Psychology Service at Guild NHS Trust in Preston, and Professor of Mental Health in the Department of Sociology, Social Policy and Social Work at the University of Liverpool.

Mina Sassoon is an independent community activist, trainer and consultant. She also works part-time for Core Arts, an innovative arts-based mental health project in Hackney.

Ann Shiers is a district nurse.

David Shiers is a general practitioner and Primary Care Mental Health Lead for West Midlands Partnerships in Mental Health.

Dawn Wakeling is Director of Quality and Standards for Mind.

Contact is a Brighton-based initiative for adults who have experienced mental health problems and is dedicated to the making of photographs on the theme of mental health and mental illness. It evolved from a photography group which is part of the Satellite Services of South Downs Health NHS Trust. Contact sets out to promote empowerment through personal exploration in relation to image making. We endeavour to produce informative and quality work which reflects contemporary issues in the field of mental health and can be exhibited in both psychiatric-related and public spaces.

Dedication

This book is dedicated to:

- all the students who took part in the piloting of the Certificate in Community Mental Health Care in Belfast, Birmingham, Blackburn, Edinburgh, Suffolk, Gwynedd and London whose help has been invaluable throughout the development of this project

- friendship of all kinds, and especially between Frances and Sharon.

Introduction

Thurstine Basset

Looking to the Future was written at the turn of the century. In this respect, it gives a 'snapshot' of mental health services across the UK as the 20th century makes way for the 21st. Authors of chapters were asked to give an up-to-date overview of the field about which they were writing. They have done this by exploring current issues and debates and referring to key research findings. They have also set the scene for the new century by examining important future challenges for mental health services.

This book is also a reader for the Certificate in Community Mental Health Care. This Certificate is a new qualification for people working in the mental health field. It has been developed by the Mental Health Foundation, working in close collaboration with City & Guilds Affinity and Pavilion Publishing. It is aimed at people who do not have a specific qualification in mental health.

The contents of the book are varied. It contains a number of photographs from Contact, a group of photographers who have experienced mental health difficulties. These photographs illustrate the book, but are not directly related to the chapters in which they appear. They are a selection taken from an exhibition 'Images of Mental Health', and are powerful statements about mental health and mental health services.

Looking to the Future **is in three parts.**

- **Part 1: Starting Points** sets the scene. David Pilgrim explores various perspectives on mental health and illness. Mo Hutchison looks at issues around empowerment, and outlines ways in which service users have been involved across mental health services. **Part 1** concludes with two chapters about carers and families. Maria Lowry and carers/relatives from the National Schizophrenia Fellowship (Northern Ireland) explain the importance of support for carers. Ann and David Shiers tell their own story, before talking about the kinds of services they would like to see in the future.

- **Part 2: Context and Frameworks** explores the legislative and policy background. Margaret Pedler lays out the legal context across the UK at a time when mental health legislation is under review. Steve Morgan and Su Akbar-Khan explore the principles and the practice of care planning across the UK. Steve Morgan then follows this with a chapter on risk and safety, looking at both risk assessment and risk management. Loretta Fuller outlines how anti-racist practices in mental health assessment have enhanced the work of a service for Black people with mental health problems. The final contribution in this part of the book comes from Dawn Wakeling, who explains quality assurance and how it can be used to improve services.

- **Part 3: Ways of Working** looks at approaches to working with people with mental health problems. Alison Murray gives a broad overview of the community support worker's role and the position of these workers in services. Jo Borrill focuses on developments in treatment and methods of preventing relapse in working with people with long-term needs. Alison Faulkner then outlines the innovative work of the Strategies for Living Project, which is a user-led programme of work at the Mental Health Foundation. Steve Onyett highlights and reviews the central importance of effective working relationships between service users and staff. Roger Moss explores the soul of psychiatry, and makes a plea for a more spiritual approach to mental health work.

Frank Bangay's poems appear throughout the book and speak eloquently of stigma and prejudice, with the buds of survival and hope forcing their way through to the light.

Mina Sassoon's poem, *Re-Defining the Code of Honour* is a fitting end to the book, and is dedicated to the Asian women she has worked with and to the community-based organisations that helped them realise their strengths.

The core principles that underpin the Certificate in Community Mental Health Care are reflected throughout this book. They can be summarised as:

- the importance of respecting and acknowledging diversity and cultural identity in our society
- service users having access to, and a choice of, appropriate and useful management and treatment approaches
- the expertise and experience of service users and families/carers being acknowledged as valid and important
- mental health services empowering service users, supporting families/carers and being aimed at, and accessible to, those in greatest need
- mental health services being integrated and cost-effective, within a spirit of co-operation amongst all the various workers and stakeholders
- a skilled and competent workforce being the bedrock of safe, sound and supportive services
- a spirit of social inclusion which constantly fights stigma, prejudice and discrimination.

Continuums in Mental Health/Breadth and Diversity

In seeking to make sense of the various approaches and opinions within the mental health field, the diagram *Continuums in Mental Health* (see overleaf) was developed as part of the Certificate.

The Continuums in Mental Health – What? Why? How? – Getting your head round the differences

This diagram relates to various key themes throughout the first three units of the Certificate in Community Mental Health Care. It attempts to show relationships between the themes which are all on a continuum of their own.

People: physical —————— psychological —————— social

Models: organic/disease —————— psychodynamic–behavioural–cognitive —————— social —————— political

Causes: neuroscientific/genetic —————— vulnerability/stress —————— oppression/racism/poverty

Approaches:
medication —————— talking treatments —————— early intervention —————— self-management
cure/contain therapies psycho-education complementary approaches
mental illness recovery/involving valorisation
family and carers promote mental health

Professions/workers:
psychiatrists —————— therapists —————— the mental health team —————— sociologists —————— campaigners
made up of various professions community survivors
and support workers workers

Society/Government:
take the pills, comply —————— health and social care work together —————— reduce stigma; social inclusion
safe, sound, supportive; using evidence-based treatments
money & power base that work, and a common language

Service users: LISTEN TO US—CHOICE OF RELEVANT APPROACHES & TREATMENTS (SAFE, SOUND & SUPPORTIVE FOR US)

Involve —————— include —————— respect us and our cultural identity —————— we are experts

equality & responsibility —————— empower us —————— each individual seeks their own explanation

The diagram tries to show the breadth and diversity of the mental health field. To understand what lies along the various continuums is a task for the mental health worker. Workers have to make sense of the tensions that exist between different models and approaches in order to work with others within the broad field of mental health. The Certificate aims to explore the various points on the continuums as part of clarifying the overall picture.

Service users are the foundation to the diagram as they seek an explanation for the situation in which they find themselves. It is only by listening to them and responding to their needs that workers can begin to be helpful to service users. The ever more potent voice of service users in the mental health field is surely the single most important factor to build on in the future.

Looking back 25 years, I still recall with some trepidation the day in 1974 that a red-faced and angry man burst into my office in the large psychiatric hospital where I worked. He was angry because I had sent him a letter of support for two nurses, who had written a well-produced and highly reasonable report which was critical of the hospital's policy. He was the Chief Nursing Officer. He spent a great deal of time telling me details of these nurses' private and political lives in order to persuade me that they could not be taken seriously. His final point – his *coup de grace* – was to inform me that both nurses had undergone psychological tests before joining the hospital, and that he had re-examined these. The tests, together with feedback he had received from others, showed, he stated, that these two nurses were in fact 'mentally ill', and for this reason alone nothing that they said could be taken seriously.

If I had said to him ' "Listen, *mate*, in 25 years' time, patients will be writing editorials in nursing journals', he would have dismissed me as crazy, from another planet. Yet in May 1999, the editorial in the journal, *Mental Health Nursing* explored the topic of evidence-based medicine. It began, *What is the evidence that the medication I am taking is working?* It was written by a service user, Alison Faulkner, Project Manager of Strategies for Living.

Attitudes can and do change. There is a long way to go in mental health, but some important steps have been made along the path.

Looking to the Future aims to be both critical and hopeful. It is written for mental health workers, some of whom may themselves be service users or carers. It acknowledges different opinions and perspectives. It strives for partnership and co-operation, but also acknowledges that these states are often hard to achieve. Overall, it aims to facilitate a better understanding amongst all involved in the mental health field. This is a small but important goal I hope we have achieved.

Starting Points

That Old Taboo

I seem to wear that old taboo
How about you?
Is it the look in my eyes?
Yes, the medication can make them a bit strange
Is it the sound of my voice?
Yes, sometimes I get nervous and stutter.
Or do you just see me as a dimwit
Who knows nothing?

We get on the same bus
Sometimes I get funny looks
When I show the driver my travel pass
We walk down the same street
Holding on to our masks.

Do you want me to hang my head in shame
Like a misunderstood child
Being made to wear a dunce's cap?

'Off to the corner
Not a word out of you
We appoint ourselves judges
Of what is good
And what is bad
We've no time to listen.'

Here comes that old taboo
Does it get to you too?
Do you see danger in my eyes?
Do you hear violence in my voice?
Do you just read the newspapers?
Can you see what lies beneath?

An untold history
Many years' struggle for rights
Survivors of the psychiatric system
We're going to keep on surviving
While we mourn for those that the struggle wore out.

So I will fight that old taboo
Will you see the need to keep fighting too?
Or will you reinforce stereotypes
That divide and control?

Can we find a place
Where our logics can meet?
Or will we go on talking through bars and windows?
Never understanding
Never understanding
That old taboo
That old taboo
Born out of fascist theories
Why can't we be looking forward
Thinking of the day when people can talk as equals
And feel compassion for each other
Can I believe this possible?

That old taboo
That old taboo
It's here to oppress
Me and you
That old taboo
That old taboo
I will keep fighting
That old taboo.
We will keep fighting
That old taboo.

Frank Bangay, Late June/early July 1998

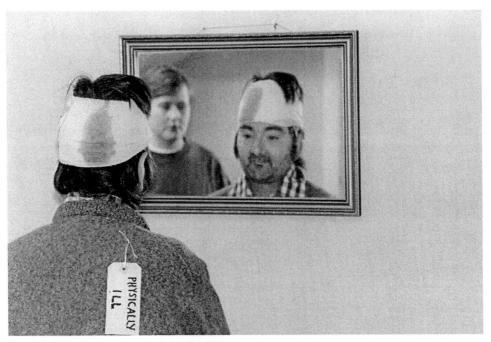

I'm Not Well 1   *David Arnold*

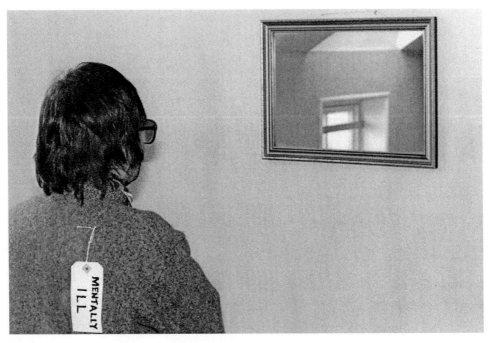

I'm Not Well 2   *David Arnold*

Chapter 1

Perspectives on mental health and illness

David Pilgrim

This chapter presents several perspectives on mental health and illness (especially the latter). It is important to note at the outset that each perspective has its strengths and weaknesses and that sometimes the various viewpoints are not describing the same phenomena. In other words, mental health and mental illness are *concepts* which are the focus of disagreement and debate within and between different groups of lay people, mental health professionals and academic researchers. Much more is written about mental health *problems* (and 'mental distress', 'mental abnormality', 'mental illness' and 'psychopathology') than mental *health*. Mental health services are actually for people diagnosed as being mentally ill or having mental health problems. However, this is little different from the NHS as a whole, which, despite its title, is by and large, an *illness* service and not a *health* service at all.

The perspectives covered are only described in summary. A fuller, more critical account of each is provided in Chapter 1 of **A Sociology of Mental Health and Illness** (Pilgrim, D. & Rogers, A. [1999] Open University Press).

The perspectives summarised in this chapter are:

- the lay view
- psychiatry
- psychoanalysis
- psychology
- the legal framework
- social causation
- labelling theory
- critical theory
- social constructivism
- social realism.

The Lay View

In every culture there is some notion of emotional or psychological difference. Not all cultures identify these differences in exactly the same way, nor do they use identical terms. But equally, no culture is indifferent to those who are sad, frightened or unintelligible in their conduct.

Most of us can identify for ourselves when we are sad or anxious. All of us might be directly involved in invoking a medical diagnosis for a friend, relative or even a stranger in the street acting in a way we find perplexing or distressing. Any of us might reach a point where we decide our distress warrants a visit to the doctor or other expert for help.

Everyday notions of 'nervousness' suggest that a concept does prefigure a psychiatric label of phobic anxiety or some other version of neurosis. Likewise, if people act in a way others cannot readily understand they run the risk of being dismissed as 'a nutter', 'a loony', 'crazy', 'mad' or even simply 'mental'. In the past few years in Britain, the term 'mental distress' has found favour with service users. A problem with this is that it alludes only to the pain of the patient and it gives no notion that they can be distressing, frustrating or frightening to others at times.

Psychiatry

Psychiatry is a specialty within medicine. Its practitioners, as in other **specialties**, are trained to see their role as identifying sick individuals (diagnosis); predicting the future course of their illness (prognosis); speculating about its cause (aetiology); and prescribing a response to the condition, to cure it or ameliorate its symptoms (treatment). Consequently, it would be surprising if psychiatrists did not think in terms of illness when they encounter variations in conduct which are troublesome to people (be they the identified patient or those upset by them). Those psychiatrists who have rejected this illness framework, in whole or part, tend to have been exposed to – and accepted – an alternative view derived from another perspective (psychology, philosophy or sociology).

As with other branches of medicine, psychiatrists vary in their assumptions about diagnosis, prognosis, aetiology and treatment. However, this does not imply that views are evenly spread throughout the profession. Western psychiatry is an eclectic enterprise. However, it does have dominant features. In particular, diagnosis is considered to be a worthy ritual for the bulk of the profession, and biological causes are favoured along with biological treatments.

Psychiatrists have used classification systems which have varied over time and place. Broadly speaking, Western psychiatry during the 20th century described three main categories of mental abnormality:

1. **psychoses** (schizophrenia, affective psychoses and organic psychoses)
2. **neuroses** (anxiety states, neurotic depression, dissociative disorder and obsessive compulsive disorder)

3. abnormal personality development (the personality disorders).

With the exception of the organic psychoses – for instance, those caused by toxic reactions, drug effects or tertiary syphilis – all of the other states have no known biological cause or signs. These *functional* disorders constitute the great bulk of the work of psychiatry.

Psychoanalysis

Like other forms of psychology, psychoanalysis works on a continuum principle – abnormality and normality are connected, not disconnected and separate. To the psychoanalsyt we are all ill to some degree. However, the medical roots of psychoanalysis and the continued dominance of medical analysts within its culture have arguably left it within a psychiatric, not psychological, discourse. It still uses the terminology of pathology ('psychopathology' and its 'symptoms'). Assessments are 'diagnostic' and its clients 'patients'. People do not merely have ways of avoiding human contact, they have 'schizoid defences'. They do not simply get into the habit of angrily blaming others all the time, instead they are 'fixated in the paranoid position'. The language of psychoanalysis is saturated with psychiatric terms. Thus the discipline of psychoanalysis stands somewhere between psychiatry and psychology.

Psychology

Psychologists have put forward a variety of ideas about mental normality/abnormality. Thus, there is not one psychological perspective but several. Four main ones are described in the next few pages.

Looking to the Future © Pavilion Publishing/Mental Health Foundation, 2000

1 The statistical notion

The statistical notion simply says that frequently-occurring behaviours in a population are normal – so infrequent behaviours are not normal. Take as an example the tempo at which people speak. Up to a certain speed, speech would be called 'normal'; above it and the person might be considered to be 'high' in ordinary parlance, or 'hypomanic' or 'suffering from pressure of thought' in psychiatric language; below a certain speed and the person might be described as 'depressed'. Most people would speak at a pace between these upper and lower points of frequency.

A question begged, of course, is: Who decides on the cut-offs at each end of the frequency distribution of speech speed? How are those decisions made? In other words, the notion of frequency in itself tells us nothing about when a behaviour is to be judged as normal or abnormal. Value judgements are required on the part of lay people or professionals when punctuating the difference between normality and abnormality. Also, a statistical notion may not hold good across cultures, even within the same country. Slow speech might be the norm in one culture, in, say rural areas, but not in another, such as the inner city.

The statistical notion of normality tells us nothing in itself about why some deviations are noted when they are uni-directional rather than bi-directional. The example of speech speed referred to bi-directional judgements. Take, in contrast, the notion of intelligence. Brightness is valued at one end of the distribution but not at the other. Being bright will not lead, in itself, to a person entering the patient role, but being dim may well do so.

2 The ideal notion of normality

There are two versions of this: one from psychoanalysis and the other from humanistic psychology. In the former case, normality is defined by a predominance of conscious over unconscious characteristics in the person. In the latter case, the ideal person is one who fulfils their human potential (or 'self-actualises').

Positive notions of mental health include:

- balance of psychic forces
- self-actualisation
- resistance to stress
- autonomy
- competence
- perception of reality.

3 Specific behaviours

The term 'maladaptive behaviour' is part of this psychological discourse, as is 'unwanted' or 'unacceptable' behaviour. The strength of this position is that it makes its criteria for what constitutes 'abnormality' explicit. The weakness is that it leaves values and norms *im*plicit. The terminology of specific behaviours still begs questions about what constitutes 'maladaptive'. Who decides what is 'unwanted' or 'unacceptable'? One party may want a behaviour to occur or find it acceptable but another may not. In these circumstances, those who have more power will tend to be the definers of reality. Thus, what constitutes unwanted behaviour is not self-evident but socially negotiated. Consequently it reflects both the power relationships and the value system operating in a culture at a point in time. This approach in psychology was linked to behaviour therapy or behaviour modification.

4 Distorted cognitions

Whilst many psychologists focus on behaviour, others focus on thought processes (cognitions). They treat inner events as if they are behaviours, forming the apparently incongruous hybrid of a 'cognitive-behavioural' approach to mental health problems or cognitive behaviour therapy (CBT).

The Legal Framework

Currently in Britain the law has a definition of mental disorder, which includes four separate conditions:

1 mental illness

2 mental impairment

3 severe mental impairment

4 psychopathic disorder.

The first of these is not defined; the second and third are references to people with learning difficulties who may additionally be deemed to be dangerous; the fourth refers to anti-social individuals who are 'abnormally aggressive' or manifest 'seriously irresponsible conduct'.

Because mental illness is not legally defined in mental health law, it is usually defined indirectly by psychiatric assessments of defendants or by expert witnesses. However, sometimes judges have resorted to the lay discourse.

In 1974, Judge Lawton said that the words 'mental illness' are 'ordinary words of the English language. They have no particular medical significance. They have no particular legal significance.'

Lawton was referring back to his colleague Lord Reid, who suggested, in giving evidence about a case where the defendant's mental state was being considered, that:

> *'I ask myself what would the ordinary, sensible person have said about the patient's condition in this case if he had been informed of his behaviour? In my judgement such a person would have said, "Well, the fellow is obviously mentally ill." '*

This is now called the 'man-must-be-mad' test in British law.

Social Causation

This perspective held by some sociologists and social psychiatrists essentially accepts schizophrenia or depression as legitimate diagnoses. They are given the status of facts in themselves. Once these diagnoses are accepted, questions are then asked about the role of socially-derived stress in their aetiology. The emphasis within a social causation approach is upon tracing the relationship between social disadvantage and mental illness. Given that the main indicator of disadvantage has for many sociologists been low social class and/or poverty, it is not very surprising that studies investigating this relationship have been a strong current within social studies of psychiatric populations. Social class has not been the only variable investigated within this social causation perspective. Disadvantage of other sorts, related to race, gender and age have also been of interest.

Labelling Theory

According to labelling theorists, when people deviate from conduct expected of them, a common reaction in others is to deny the deviation in order to keep the person in their existing role. However, under certain conditions ('contingencies') oddity becomes diagnosed mental illness so that the person takes on a deviant role. The transition between these two sets of circumstances can be linked to either a one-off crisis or a series of gradual shifts. The latter is a bit like water reaching boiling point after being heated for a long time. Labelling theorists describe primary deviance (rule-breaking with many causes) and secondary deviance. The latter refers to the maintenance of a deviant role because of the reaction of others (labelling). According to this view, rule-breaking leads to a deviant role which is maintained by the person's own view of themselves and the expectation of others.

As far as mental illness is concerned, labelling theorists do not concur on who are the significant labellers. For some, it is psychiatrists, for others it is the family + professionals +

the total institution. However, there is an agreement that, once labelled, this significantly alters the person's identity and social status. Once a person is seen to have lost their reason, then they will never be quite the same again in the eyes of others. They are stripped of their old identity and a new one takes its place. Thus, according to labelling theory, the psychiatric patient's role is then maintained by a new set of role expectations. The person in the patient role plays at being a patient and those looking on construe all of the person's conduct in terms of the patient role. However, this can be disrupted by new contingencies emerging.

Critical Theory

During the 20th century, a number of writers attempted to account for the relationship between socio-economic conditions and mental life. Critical theory (or the 'Frankfurt School') was an example of this – an attempt to integrate the broad ideas of Freud and Marx. Critical theory is exemplified in studies of the authoritarian personality; the mass psychology behind the cessation of protest, the theory of art, and the critique of science in capitalist societies.

Social Constructivism

One of the most influential theoretical positions evident in the sociology of health and illness over the last 20 years of the 20th century was social constructivism – it sometimes appears as 'social constructionism', especially, though not only, in psychological literature. A central assumption within this broad approach is that reality is not self-evident, stable and waiting to be discovered, but instead it is a product of human activity.

Constructivists problematise the factual status of mental illness. They analyse the ways in which mental health work has been linked to the production of psychiatric knowledge and the production of mental health problems. Mental illness is not seen as a fact inside patients. Instead it is understood as a by-product or artefact of psychiatry. Also, they establish the links which exist in modern society with the coercive control of deviance by psychiatry on the one hand and the production of selfhood by mental health expertise on the other. They are as much concerned with the ways in which mental health work (the 'psy complex') produces the self as with the ways in which it crushes it in modern society.

Social Realism

It is clear that the assumptions of social causationism and social constructivism are incompatible. The first takes the reality of psychiatric illness at face value, whereas the second depicts it as an artefact of professional activity. A compromise position is offered by social (or 'critical' or 'sceptical') realism. This accepts the existence of material reality but argues that social processes (including the diagnosis of mental illness) reflect the interests of some groups (the psychiatric profession, non-patients) and subordinate the interests of powerless groups like people with mental health problems. Social realism thus would accept that knowledge derived from natural science might help our understanding of the functioning of the brain and its impact on behaviour (like social causationists who accept that people may be biologically vulnerable to mental illness) but it would also emphasise that the diagnosis of mental illness is a social negotiation which reflects power relationships in society (like social constructivism and labelling theory). Unlike the social causationists, the social realists take a sceptical look at psychiatric knowledge and the interests which it serves.

Summary/Discussion

It can be seen from this overview of different perspectives about mental normality and abnormality that each provides its own particular set of descriptions and contains different assumptions. For example, in the psychiatric view, people are either ill or not ill – the medical model emphasises discontinuity. By contrast, psychologists emphasise continuity between normal and abnormal phenomena. Psychoanalysts insist that we are all ill to some degree. Sociologists vary in their emphases. The social causationists are uncritical of psychiatric diagnoses and are mainly interested in which social forces *cause* people to become ill. Labelling theorists are agnostic about the primary causes of deviance but they focus on the way in which the reaction of others labels and then maintains a deviant identity. Social constructivists focus more on the activity of psychiatrists than the patients they diagnose. They go further than the labelling theorists. For the labelling theorist it is secondary deviance which is socially negotiated.

All of this complexity should caution us against the idea that there *is* a single reality (say, mental illness) which different perspectives have a view about. Each perspective constructs its own particular reality, warrants one type of reality or privileges one reality over another. In other words, this is not like talking about cars, automobiles or motor vehicles – in that instance a commonly agreed referent or object is described by different words. By contrast, when we talk about mental health and mental illness, these concepts invite a whole range of assumptions about their nature and causality. It is these underlying assumptions which may or may not be compatible.

From the series "In Sanity": Deteriorating Faculties *Pierre M.*

From the series "In Sanity": Tranquility of Mind *Pierre M.*

Looking to the Future © Pavilion Publishing/Mental Health Foundation, 2000

Chapter 2

Issues around user empowerment

Mo Hutchison

Explanation of Terms

'User'

A variety of terms have been employed to describe people who use mental health services: patient, client, consumer, user, survivor. There have been objections to all of these terms and much thought has been given to seeking the ideal term. It does not seem to exist although 'user' has been most generally adopted. However, the bottom line has to be that people who use mental health services define themselves in a way that is most acceptable to them.

Mind defines 'users' as:

> '...people who have themselves used any services (such as inpatient, out-patient or primary care) because they experience, or are thought by others to experience, emotional distress or 'mental illness.'

Mind Policy on User Involvement, 1993

For the sake of clarity and consistency this is the term used throughout this chapter.

Empowerment

An American psychologist, Rappaport, studied empowerment and concluded that it involved individual determination over one's own life and democratic participation in the life of one's community. Within mental health services, as within much of medicine, empowerment has not been the name of the game. There has been a prevailing ethos of 'doctor knows best':

> *'There is a pervasive societal belief that trained professionals are the only people who know how to provide proper assistance. This attitude exists whether our television needs to be fixed or we need help dealing with personal issues. We have grown accustomed to turning to professionals for help because we assume they have special expertise.'*

Besio *et al*, 1987

To an extent this is understandable as we often approach doctors at a time when we are vulnerable and worried and want to feel that we can safely 'put our lives in their hands'. Traditionally, decisions about people's care and treatment – even far-reaching decisions – are made *about* rather than *with* people. As has been stated, this paternalism exists in all health services. However, in *mental* health services this is often compounded by the belief that the service users are incapable of taking part in decision-making.

It is, perhaps, even more important that people with mental health problems are involved in decisions about their care and treatment as these may have a profound effect on their lives. The rest of this paper will examine why empowerment within mental health services has become a necessary force and how it might best be achieved.

Introduction

Professor Ivan Illich described the mid-twentieth century as
The Age of Disabling Professions (Illich *et al*, 1977):

> *'...an age when people had "problems", experts had
> "solutions" and scientists measured imponderables, such as
> "abilities" and "needs".'*

John McKnight (1977) argues that this was because
professionals were in a position to define need, remedy, and
assessment of outcome which, ultimately, led to the user
being 'disabled'. Nowhere was this more evident than within
mental health services.

And then there came the heady, protest-led days of the
1960s and '70s when the very foundations of the establishment
were being attacked. So-called anti-psychiatrists – such as
R. D. Laing and Thomas Szasz – were even questioning the
basic premises on which the existence of 'mental illness' were
built.

Against such a fertile background it is not surprising that
those people who considered that they had been 'disabled' by
mental health services began to identify themselves with
those within the civil rights movements, particularly around
such issues as injustice and oppression. Recognising the
wisdom in the Trade Union adage 'Unity is Strength',
organisations such as the Campaign Against Psychiatric
Oppression and the British Network for Alternatives to
Psychiatry were formed. The 1980s and '90s saw the
formation of Survivors' Speak Out (1986), the United
Kingdom Advocacy Network (1992) and the establishment
of Mindlink, the user body within Mind (1990).

At the same time, the political emphasis was very squarely
being put on 'consumerism'. Consumers became important
people to be wooed and consulted rather than patronised or
ignored.

> *'The policy message has been consistent throughout the
> 1990s, with each major document (eg DoH, SSI, 1994)*

stressing the importance of involving users in service design and delivery.'

Peck & Barker, 1997

The reality of this consultation might be more problematic but it did give users and user organisations a forum in which their voices might be heard:

'The empowerment movement within mental health has challenged the traditional picture and encouraged the gap between service providers and users to close by sharing information and decision-making.'

Bates, 1991

The Routes to Empowerment

If users are to regain some control over their lives there needs to be a shift in the balance of power between themselves and mental health professionals:

'...shifting power relationships will pose many dilemmas for professionals who, while they may often feel powerless, are nevertheless used to having the power to determine what they think is right for "their patients".'

Perkins & Repper, 1998

The key element to achieving this shift is to involve service users at all levels of the mental health system: in the planning of their own support; in the design and running of statutory and independent services; in the recruitment of staff; in the training of mental health professionals; in monitoring the effectiveness of services; in researching and evaluating services and, finally, in the establishment of user-run or user-led services.

Involving Users in the Planning and Delivery of their Own Care and Treatment

It is paradoxical that some statutory agencies have sophisticated and apparently effective mechanisms for involving users in such matters as planning future services but deny to those in their care the basic right of involvement in planning their own support – a sacred cow indeed! With the introduction of care planning the structures should be in place for users to have a greater influence over what is to happen to them, when and by whom it is done. The reality of this influence is still very much guided by the policies and practices of individual agencies. Many professionals do not share power readily and may deem users incapable or uninterested in assisting in drawing-up their care plans. Alternatively, their views may be discounted as being unrealistic or a function of their mental health problems. These perceptions are rarely true but users do need to be provided with information, support and advocacy in order to make participation meaningful.

Users also need to be involved in the reviews of care plans as they are uniquely placed to feed back on what has been successful or unsuccessful in the arrangements for their care and treatment. They also can provide information on unmet need – information so crucial to service planners and commissioners.

The use of crisis cards and advance directives for mental health crises is gaining more impetus. Survivors Speak Out described how a user *'when in a rational state of mind, can set out in writing how they would like to be treated in circumstances when they are not the best judge of their own interests'*.

While the Government encourages the informal use of crisis cards, they have yet to provide for them to be legally effective. This is certainly a measure which would allow a user to retain some control even when at his/her most vulnerable.

Information as a Personal Resource

With reference to their own care, users must be informed of their rights. This information should be imparted in written form but also in a verbal, face-to-face form. Information also needs to be provided on different treatment options and the differential benefits and potential disadvantages of each treatment.

> *'Some patients will be capable of using much more detailed and specific information than others. The Royal College of Nursing view is that the amount of information given should always err in the patient's favour.'*

Letter from RCN to Mind, 1991

Psychiatrists often shy away from giving too much information about medication particularly with regard to short and long-term side effects. The provision of information should not be contingent upon how it is used or what conclusions are reached. Self-determination is a basic human right, and the reality is that there is already some legislation in place – and likely to be more – for situations where that right conflicts with the rights of others or where the user concerned is not deemed to be capable of making accurate judgements. If 'informed consent' is to be a reality, it is incumbent on mental health professionals to provide information on options and to support users in making choices (advocacy too has a role here; see opposite).

It is also crucial to ensure that accessible information is provided for users whose first language is not English.

Advocacy as a Personal Resource

'A civilisation is measured by its treatment of its most vulnerable groups. We must remember that citizens in care are no less citizens and their voices should be heard, their views respected and their interests defended.'

Edna Conlan, 1990

From this quote, UKAN's Code of Practice goes on to say that *'the aim of advocacy is to enable those things to happen in the most direct and empowering ways'*.

When using mental health services it is often difficult for users to assert themselves and make their views known. Advocates are a source of information and support and having such a person present frequently eases the process of involvement and empowerment. In addition, many advocacy schemes are particularly well-equipped to assist users from minority ethnic groups.

UKAN defines a number of different types of advocacy:

- **legal advocacy** – representation by legally qualified advocates, usually solicitors

- **citizen advocacy** – a long-term, one-to-one partnership between user and advocate

- **formal advocacy** – usually refers to schemes run by voluntary groups where advocates are paid

- **peer advocacy** – support from advocates who themselves use or have used mental health services

The cornerstones of any advocacy scheme are that it must be independent and assist users in working towards self-advocacy.

Involving Users

Involving users in planning services

It has become relatively commonplace to allocate one or two seats on mental health service-planning committees to service users but again if it is to be meaningful it has to be a *well-thought out and honestly enacted procedure'* (Hutchison *et al*, 1993). Otherwise it may be viewed as a tokenistic gesture which has no real impact. There are various ways of reducing the possibility of tokenism:

- ensure that there is more than one user on the committee
- ensure that all user-members are familiar with the workings of committees; provide training if not
- ensure that all user-members have access to the same information as all other committee members
- ensure this information is clear and jargon-free or ensure that any jargon is explained
- ensure that user-members have access to support if needed
- pay users for their involvement unless they receive payment from another source
- be clear and honest about any areas or issues which users cannot influence.

Involving users in the recruitment of staff

Many voluntary mental health service-providers and some statutory agencies now involve users in staff selection. In these days of Equal Opportunities Policies (EOP) such involvement is usually formalised and users are part of selection panels so that they can take part in the discussion and decision as to the most suitable candidate. It is clear once again that – in order for such involvement to be meaningful – users (as with other panel members) need training on staff selection procedures under EOP.

Involving users in training mental health professionals

The role of users as a training resource for mental health professionals is increasingly being acknowledged. It has the potential to:

- challenge some of the myths around mental health problems
- allow users and workers to discuss potential dilemmas
- provide a safe environment for controversial issues to be explored.
- enable those who are responsible for delivering mental health services to gain an insight into what it is like to be on the receiving end of such services.

However, there are necessary conditions which need to exist if user-trainers and their trainees are to benefit from the experience:

- user input needs to be integrated within the training as a whole
- all relevant information must be provided to user-trainers well in advance
- the course co-ordinator must take responsibility for ensuring that students give adequate and equal attention to user input
- support must be provided for user-trainers
- user-trainers must be paid in the same way and at the same level as other trainers.

Involving users in monitoring and researching services

As with the involvement of users in training courses, any activity which alters the negative status of users from being passive recipients of services (which frequently dwell on their inadequacies and needs) to a more positive status (of being valued and valuable colleagues) is likely to have an empowering effect.

Apart from the monitoring role undertaken by Patients' Councils and some user groups, involvement of users in monitoring services is at an early stage of development.

However, this approach is being championed by organisations such as the Sainsbury Centre for Mental Health which has established a user-focused monitoring system to embed the user perspective in quality assurance.

Employing users as researchers is, as yet, under-developed. However, a survivors' research group has recently been established under the auspices of the Mental Health Foundation. Other mental health organisations have user-consultants who may carry out research.

Involving users as providers of services

While the UK has something of a tradition of self-help, the development of user-led services has been rather slow, perhaps because of the perceived threat they might pose to other service-providing agencies. However, there are now a variety of user-run services which are described by Lindow (1994). Crisis services, including helplines and crisis houses, are considered by users and some professionals to be particularly amenable to being run by other users.

This aspect of user involvement is another area that is rich in potential and it is likely that this potential will be concentrated on providing alternative services which are so valued by users.

Conclusion

'Empowerment is not a scarce resource that gets used up'

Rappaport, 1987

Power does not lend itself to being handed out like so much lost property. The aim must be to create environments and situations where users can take power back for themselves by being involved in realistic and meaningful ways.

The user movement is continually faced with dilemmas, such as whether to adopt a pragmatic approach and risk diluting its own agenda, or to become more forceful campaigners and risk alienating other users and allies. Added to this is a climate in which the general public, incited by irresponsible sections of the media, is becoming more fearful of people with severe mental health problems living in the community. It seems likely that this will result in more coercive treatment proposals from the Government. Against such a background, the potential for mental health service users to assert their rights becomes more problematic.

It is also undeniable that the level of user involvement in some mental health agencies is still tokenistic where the user voice is frequently discounted or marginalised. Many users express doubts about the willingness of mental health services to give users decision-making powers. However, the call for greater democracy within mental health services is not one which is going to be silenced. The only questions are the extent and pace of such democratisation. Time will tell.

References

Bates, P. (1991) *Just Another Seat on the Committee: Training and User Involvement in Mental Health Services*. London: NHS Training Directorate.

Besio, S., Blach, A., & Quinn, K. (1987) *The Role of Ex-Patients and Consumers in Human Resource Development for the 1990s*. Centre for Community Change Through Housing and Support, Burlington, VT.

Campbell, P. (1996) The History of the User Movement in the United Kingdom. In: T.Heller *et al* (Eds) *Mental Health Matters*. Milton Keynes: Open University Press.

Hutchison, M., Linton, G. & Lucas, J. (1993) *User Involvement Information Pack*. London: Mind Publications.

Illich, I., Zola, I., McNight, J., Caplan, J. & Shaiken, H. (1977) *Disabling Professions*. London: Marion Boyars Publishers Ltd.

Lindow, V. (1994) *Purchasing Mental Health Services: Self-Help Alternatives*. London: Mind Publications.

Mind (1993) *Policy on User Involvement*. London: Mind

McKnight, J. (1977) Professionalized Services and Disabling Help. In: *Disabling Professions* pp69-73. London: Marion Boyars Publishers Ltd.

Peck, E. & Barker, I. (1997) Users as Partners in Mental Health - Ten Years of Experience. *Journal of Interprofessional Care* 11 369-77.

Perkins, R. & Repper, J. (1998) *Dilemmas in Community Mental Health Practice: Choice or Control.* Oxfordshire: Radcliffe Medical Press Ltd.

Rappaport, J. (1987) Term of empowerment/exemplars of prevention: toward a theory for community psychology. *American Journal of Community* Psychology **15** 1.

Additional reading/resources

Barker, I. (1991) *Power Games: Workshop on user empowerment in mental health services.* Brighton: Pavilion Publishing.

Beeforth, M., Conlan, E. & Graley, R. (1994) *Have We Got Views For You: User Evaluation of Case Management.* London: The Sainsbury Centre for Mental Health.

Chamberlin, J. (1988) *On Our Own: Patient-controlled Alternatives to the Mental Health System.* London: Mind Publications.

Hart, L. (1995) *Phone at Nine Just to Say You're Alive.* Douglas Elliot Press.

Leader, A. (1995) *Direct Power: A Resource Pack For People Who Want to Develop Their Own Care Plans and Support Networks.* Brighton: Pavilion Publishing.

McIver, S. (1991) *Obtaining the Views of Users of Mental Health Services.* London: King's Fund.

Mind Guide to Advocacy in Mental Health: Empowerment in Action (1992). In: *Mental Health: Empowerment in Action.* London: Mind publications.

Read, J. & Reynolds, J. (1996) *Speaking Our Minds: An Anthology of Personal Experiences of Mental Distress and its Consequences.* Milton Keynes: Open University Press.

Read, J. & Wallcraft, J. (1992) *Guidelines for Empowering Users of Mental Health Services.* London: UNISON/Mind.

Stigma No. 3

My cause?
Well my cause
Is to annoy you,
You with your false ethics
And taboos.

You see
I just can't believe these things,
I've seen too much
of the harm they cause.

My cause?
Yes; it's to make myself a nuisance
to you who sit around
saying 'isn't it terrible
but what can we do about it,
all those poor people and their misery?'
so we just let them scream in silence.

It starts with a joke about
a harmless little joke about...

You see
I believe in causing a fuss –
at least we can turn a head
here or there,
make someone think,
help someone on their way;
if that is being a nuisance,
then that is what I want to be.

It starts with a rejection
of somebody
who doesn't walk on familiar lines,
somebody whose ideas
are not so conventional
as society would like,
somebody whose face doesn't fit.

Then the professionals come in
With textbook theories.
It starts with a joke about,
A harmless little poke about...

Label No. 1
is to make you feel put down,
not quite so good
as your so-called 'sane' friends.

Label No. 2
is to categorise you
as 'mentally ill'
so they can control you, or me, or you.

Stigma No. 3
Is to cut you off from society
as a deviant
who has committed no crime,
just spoken
his or her mind
about a situation full of absurd impossibilities;
but I'm sure you'll feel the strain
of living,
just like me.

Anyway,
what is a rebel?
and what are we conforming to?

My cause?
Well, it's through experience
not choice,
but it is
to keep on making a noise.
About our weird class ethics:
you see
I don't believe
that anyone is inferior
to anybody,
but I see the ways
we react to situations,
and the ways they condemn rebelling.

My cause?
Well, it is to keep on believing
that people can rid themselves
of the image
of being thick,
with support
and encouragement.

But you hear those theories
about somebody's inferior sperm,
the guilt and the shame
dumped on to
those who are born poor;
it's an ancient myth,
it's just practised more subtly now.

My fight
is to smash the myth
of mental illness.

It starts with a joke about,
a lot of gobbledegook about…

First they bring on someone
less able to be articulate,
then they tell them
that they are illiterate,
then they bring on the psychologist
with a smiling mask
and a pat on the head
and a sweet to suck -
'There's a good boy.'
'There's a good girl.'

First it starts with a joke about,
a harmless little poke about -
'HA HA.'

Label No. 1
Go on, dump on someone,
I know it makes you feel good,
I'm sure you can cleanse your conscience.

Label No. 2
Is meant to control you
with a label of 'mental illness'
and token gestures of niceness;
but I'm sure you can see,
through the mist,
one or two truths
refuse to be covered up.

Stigma No. 3
Is meant for all humanity -
at some time in our lives
things won't work quite right.

First it starts with just a little joke about,
a dig and a poke about.

Aim 1
Don't be put down.

Aim 2
Pick yourself up off the ground.

Aim 3
Believe in yourself.

BELIEVE. BELIEVE.

Go on!
Believe in yourself.

Frank Bangay, January 1985

This poem, about Psychiatry and the Class Struggle, was partly written from personal experience. It was also inspired by an article I read in 1984, which stated how, in America in the 1950s, psychiatrists were saying how slum-dwellers, ie people from ghetto areas, were less intelligent because they were born from inferior sperm. This theory is classist and racist. It also fails to take into account issues like poor housing conditions, bad education, or lack of access to opportunities and information. These theories are still very common in psychiatry today, an example of this being the way Black people are often viewed by psychiatry.

Don't Lose Your Head 1 *Jack Scivyer*

Don't Lose Your Head 2 *Jack Scivyer*
(Note: lack of focus is the artist's decision)

Looking to the Future © Pavilion Publishing/Mental Health Foundation, 2000

Chapter 3

Carers' testimonies

Maria Lowry

This chapter explores the work of the National Schizophrenia Fellowship (NSF) in Northern Ireland with carers and relatives of people with a diagnosis of schizophrenia.

The NSF exists to improve the lives of people affected by schizophrenia and other severe mental illnesses by providing quality support, services and information and by influencing local, regional and national policies.

The organisation was first established in 1972 by carers of individuals experiencing schizophrenia. This came about as a result of a letter written by a carer being published in *The Times*. The letter stated the carer's position – looking after a son with schizophrenia – and the dismay, frustration and isolation he felt at the lack of information and education available in relation to the illness. The letter requested that anyone in a similar position contact him to discuss a way forward in relation to their problems.

The carer was inundated with responses. Whilst this provided a comfort, in the knowledge that he was not alone, it also highlighted the fact that there was a very large number of people in similar circumstances. It was recognised that something had to be developed to support people and help address their needs and so the National Schizophrenia Fellowship was formed.

The NSF Northern Ireland was formed in 1980 under similar circumstances. On hearing of the English experience, a Northern Irish carer placed an advertisement in the *Belfast Telegraph* requesting contact from other people who were caring for an individual with schizophrenia. Again a huge response followed and so Northern Ireland developed as a region of the National Schizophrenia Fellowship.

Since its formation, the NSF has been concerned with providing carers with information about schizophrenia and other severe and enduring mental illnesses, guiding and assisting them with the development of constructive coping strategies and helping them in their caring role through carer/relative support groups.

The following testimonies have been written by carers in Northern Ireland in relation to their needs and the support that they value from the NSF.

A Carer's View, Cookstown

'First let me say how grateful I am for this opportunity to say a big thank you to the members and staff of the Cookstown NSF Carers group, for the friendship, help and support shown to me since I joined almost two years ago.

Anyone shouldering the burden of a family member who has schizophrenia would benefit greatly from the support of a carer's group as early as possible into the illness.

I can only describe my experience as a nightmare. Thinking you're alone in all of this, not knowing how to cope. After my son was discharged from hospital I was left with this eggshell, or time bomb, not sure how far I should push or if indeed I should. Life for my son, my family and myself could have been so different had I known that just a short distance away, a group of carers such as myself met once a month to help each other with all of the very same problems I was facing alone. The fact of realising that you're not the only family to be hit by this terrible illness is very helpful and learning of many cases worse than your own.

Most encouraging to me was meeting a young man who has schizophrenia, and was successful in doing 'A' levels and moving onto college.

The bond between the carers brings you in from the cold. We have very helpful and interested speakers at our meetings, who can advise on all the various benefits available to carers and sufferers alike. We also have more informal and relaxing evenings when we can "let our hair down". We can, as a group, voice our opinions to the mental health teams and make certain that, in the future, consideration and attention is paid to the carer, ensuring better care for the sufferer.

Seek out an NSF group in your area. If there isn't one, why not start one?'

Comment from a Parent, Coleraine

'As a parent of someone who suffers from a mental illness, we receive great help and encouragement from the Carers Support Group, which meets once a month.

It is an opportunity for us to meet together with other carers, be they relatives or friends of mentally ill people. We talk and listen and share together our concerns, not only for those who are ill, but also for the carers themselves.

From time to time we also have the opportunity to speak and listen to those professionally involved with mentally ill people, such as psychiatrists, CPNs, social workers etc. Their information and advice is most valuable to carers.

We would encourage all carers of mentally ill people to make use of this support.'

A Carer's Thoughts, Antrim

'I have been a member of a small support group in Antrim for a number of years. When my son first became ill, I needed a lot of answers that the professionals were unable to give

me. I felt really apprehensive about joining a support group, as I thought this meant I was weak and I couldn't look after my son without help. Since attending the group I have found that a lot of my feelings were the same as other carers and I am not a "freak" who made my son ill. I also found that when living with someone who has schizophrenia, my own natural skills for caring were not appropriate for this type of illness. It is best to learn as much as you possibly can about schizophrenia and develop new skills for caring.

I know that it is hard to join a group like this. I, myself, delayed for a number of reasons: I was ashamed at not being able to cope; I felt guilty because my son was ill; I was even hoping that the illness would just go away – but it didn't.

I would urge any carer to join a support group so that we can share skills between ourselves and can also support each other in times of need.'

What's the Use?

Comments about the value of a carer's group, Cookstown

Carers' groups – why bother?

- **care** for each member
- **combat isolation** – being a member prevents the feeling of being a lone carer
- **companionship** – meeting other carers and making new friends, who have similar problems
- **help** – group members are generally willing to help each other, even if it's only a chat by phone
- **practical help** – where needed; for example, if a carer is in need of transport in an emergency, a fellow carer may oblige
- **speakers** – periodically at monthly meetings, speakers (eg psychiatrists, nurses, occupational therapists, social workers) come to give talks and answer questions
- **benefits** – representatives from Citizens' Advice Bureau or NSF will speak and answer questions

- **entertainment** – meals out, theatre visits etc, jointly agreed by the group (no obligation to attend)
- **training facilitator** – the group is under the guidance of a very interested and hard-working person who promotes the aims of the group – and is only a phone call away

A Carer from Ballycastle highlights the benefits of a supportive group

- **being understood** – meeting and talking to people who know what you are talking about
- **gaining information** – through the expertise of the organiser through the speakers and visitors with specialist experience and training
- **access** – to a source of information, such as up-to-date research work in therapies and drugs and other resources
- **removal** – of a feeling of isolation that no-one else knows what it is like
- **opportunity** – to express fears, misunderstandings about what professionals are doing and the 'rules' which they must observe
- **a place where you can speak freely** but in confidence about your sense of failure and inadequacy, and be encouraged and strengthened; where you can share with those who are further along the road *and* with those who are not so far
- **enabling (help, preparation)** – to face the future; to meet the unsympathetic 'don't want to know' attitude of many; to overcome a sense of shame or a wish to hide, arising from the 'stigma' that is still conveyed by 'ignorant' people

Unmet Need

Despite NSF having a positive influence with many carers, there is still a huge area of unmet need.

In 1988, Sir Roy Griffiths in the Community Care Agenda for Action stated:

'A failure to give proper levels of support to informal carers not only reduces their own quality of life and that of the relative and friend they care for, but it is also potentially inefficient as it can lead to less personally-appropriate care being offered.'

A review of the literature from 1988 to the present date does not evidence a lot of improvement in terms of community care addressing the needs of carers.

The *Carers (Recognition & Services) Act 1995* gives informal carers in the UK, on request, a right to a separate assessment of their ability to care when the needs of the person they are caring for are being assessed (statutory powers in Northern Ireland).

While this Act was welcomed by NSF as a positive step to addressing carers' needs as an issue in its own right, its effect was somewhat lost as health and social services trusts, can only promote 'where resources will allow'. With health and personal social services trusts all claiming to be feeling the pinch of community-care cutbacks, few see themselves in a position to assess and provide the services required to address carers' needs.

Challenges for the Future

The *National Service Framework for Mental Health (1999)* states in its sixth standard:

'All individuals who provide regular and substantial care for a person on CPA should have an assessment of their caring, physical and mental health needs, repeated on at least an annual basis, (and) their own written care plan which is given to them and implemented in discussion with them.'

The *Modernising Health and Social Services National Priorities Guidance 1999/2002* states as its objective to *'improve users' and carers' access to services, the quality of continuing care and treatment they receive.'*

Both these Government papers indeed set challenges in relation to carers' needs being addressed.

The NSF, working jointly with the Sainsbury Centre for Mental Health, has already begun to meet these challenges by producing a Carers' Education and Support Programme (CESP). The CESP programme has been piloted by NSF in Dover and Birmingham.

CESP aims to provide a comprehensive and sustainable local education/training resource for both carers and the mental health professionals who work with them.

Designed by carers, in consultation with leading mental health professionals, the CESP programme has been built on published findings on carers' needs, psycho-social intervention and on existing good practice in carer psycho-education. CESP involves both carers and service users in providing input to programmes and has benefited greatly from the input of nurses, who have been trained in psycho-social interventions. Conclusions suggested in CESP's evaluation indicate that access to professionally-led training in symptom-management is very much welcomed by carers. The evaluation also highlighted that CESP fulfils a clearly expressed need for support in managing the everyday problems that arise in their role as carers. Carers' education courses, which offer carers general information and support, do not meet their needs in the more specific way that the CESP programme does.

The challenges for NSF Northern Ireland are:

- to promote CESP
- to educate and inform the statutory sector in Northern Ireland about its effectiveness
- to secure long-term funding for its delivery
- to ensure it is accessible to all those carers looking after an individual with a severe or enduring mental illness.

We believe that working in partnership with others, using educational programmes like CESP, will lead to greater understanding of mental illness all round and to a better quality of life for both service users and carers.

References

Carers (Recognition and Services) Act 1995. London: The Stationery Office.

Department of Health (1999) *Modernising Health and Social Services - National Priorities Guidance 1999-2002.* London: DoH.

Department of Health (1999) *National Service Framework for Mental Health.* London: The Stationery Office.

Griffiths, R. (1998) *Community Care: Agenda for Action (Griffiths Report).* London: The Stationery Office.

National Schizophrenia Fellowship/Sainsbury Centre for Mental Health (1998) *Carers Education and Support Programme (CESP) - a 10-Session Education Programme.* Published by NSF/SCMH.

Chapter 4

Who cares?

Ann & David Shiers

By offering you our perspective – that of parents to a family of three children, the eldest having a serious mental illness – we hope to explore some of the difficult issues that face other families. However we should caution the inevitable narrowness of one experience, recognising each caring situation will have its own unique story to tell.

This chapter is in two parts: **Part 1: Our Story** explores the impact that mental illness has had on our family. **Part 2: Carers' Needs and the Importance of Involvement** looks at some of the needs of carers and stresses the importance of involving carers in services.

Part 1: Our Story

When she was 17 years old, our daughter Mary was diagnosed as having schizophrenia. The illness emerged from a difficult adolescence and pitched our family into turmoil from which it is painfully and slowly recovering.

Mary was born by Caesarean at 33 weeks gestation after my wife, Ann had severe toxaemia. The twins arrived 18 months later, and I became a GP in semi-rural north Staffordshire. Mary's ambition was to ride ponies and marry a farmer. She settled into a normal school with slight developmental delay. She struggled academically, was clumsy in action and speech, and became increasingly temperamental. Psychologists diagnosed minimal birth injury, although she was capable of attending a normal school. But she was unhappy and left at 16 to attend a local learning disability farm project.

Isolated from her friends, Mary began to mutter under her breath, she had mood swings, and home life became fraught. She attempted suicide by frenziedly pushing paper into an electric socket. Bewildered, we arranged a home assessment and were astonished when the psychiatrist diagnosed schizophrenia. She was nearly 17.

A cyclical pattern soon emerged to Mary's illness, consisting of an initial phase of low mood to be gradually replaced by higher mood, and then in turn to be replaced by intense paranoid delusions towards family members and school friends. Finally her mood would plummet, the paranoia would diminish and she would become quite flat emotionally. Consequently, family life revolved round Mary's five week cycle of psychosis and weekly outpatient trips. Ann stopped district nursing to devote her time to Mary – and to her behaviour of walking incessantly, visiting grandma, shopping, swimming, baking – haunting Ann with her stock phrase – 'What shall we do now?' Friends could not visit, our sons were ignored and work became my retreat – at home I would disappear to the shed or study as Mary became increasingly paranoid towards me and her ex-school friends. At night, knives were hidden and doors locked as she would roam around the house agitated and unable to sleep.

We coped for a year without day support or an appropriate adolescent unit until Mary's paranoia suddenly extended to Ann. This necessitated urgent admission to an adult hospital ward. Forsaking our daughter to this nightmare setting fuelled our guilt but let us reflect and begin some family life again. For six months she gradually deteriorated, heavily drugged, and too ill to return home.

Her decline led to transfer to the local Victorian asylum –
2000 residents in its heyday but then, only 280. She was
admitted to an eight-bed dormitory, without curtains round
the beds or carpets. At the same time, dormitories for lads in
the local detention centre were being upgraded to individual
rooms. Mary's only sin was being ill. An enduring awareness
of this haunted Ann and me as we went off to sleep. Mary's
empty bedroom next door reminded us that she was
condemned to sleep in a comfortless, Dickensian dormitory.

Mary's rehabilitation ward – 17 clients aged between 20
and 40 – felt like an oasis in a desert of elderly residents
wondering around cadging cigarettes, swearing, lost in their
own worlds. Within a few days, an old man pushed Mary into
some bushes to kiss her and a younger, potentially violent
patient from the hospital's Challenging Unit warned Ann to
keep Mary away from him.

Now aged 18, Mary was incapable of normal thought,
incoherent, drooling, and grossly overweight. She did
nothing, went nowhere, managing only half an hour at home
over Christmas because of paranoia towards me. We
despaired for her future.

One good thing about being at rock bottom is that you
cannot sink lower. Supported by her excellent consultant we
began to fight back. Clozapine was started and proved
crucial to controlling the psychosis. Multi-agency assessment
catalogued serious unmet needs and enabled us to challenge
the system. We complained to everyone – local health
services, the Community Health Council, MPs, colleagues.
Our MP reassured us with the latest glossy Department of
Health booklet. The reality was dreadful and we grieved
through guilt, disbelief and anger.

What was Mary rehabilitating to? Our health authority
denied responsibility. Was it satisfied with its purchased
rehabilitation for an 18-year-old? It simply advised us to
await the realisation of its £20 million business plan which
would close the old 'bin' and open a new rehabilitation unit
by May 1997.

After six fruitless months locally we complained to the
West Midlands Regional Health Authority. The effect of this
one letter was remarkable. The person responsible for mental

health in the region visited us to hear our concerns. At last someone with mental health skills *and* compassion was listening. This was followed rapidly by a visit from representatives from the regional health authority to see the local facilities.

The result was that Mary's ward and two other long-stay wards were divided up, allowing some privacy. There has, however, been a continued failure to agree the closure of the hospital. When we visited excellent rehabilitation projects in Birmingham we realised what we lacked locally. Our determination and the pressure from the region persuaded the local purchasers to fund four full-time registered mental nurses for two years, and, with social services, to commission an innovative community rehabilitation project.

Once this project was up and running, Mary moved into her own flat. Now, she buys and cooks her own food, looks after her own room, plays her own music, visits a community activities resource most days and loves the local market. Her mental health is a revelation to those who remember her from the hospital and we feel proud of her again.

Part 2: Carers' Needs and the Importance of Involvement

Carers' needs

'Burden' is a word often used to describe living with someone with mental illness. We love our daughter dearly and celebrate her recovery but there is no doubting the sense of burden that we experienced, particularly in the first few years. At the very least there was a *'Why us? What have we done to deserve this?'* Many was the time we would go off to sleep doubting how we could survive another day of Mary's constant demand for attention.

The biggest impact is on the simple things we take for granted – those day-to-day activities where we relate to each other as a family, or with our friends, or at work. And then there's the stigma – feeling unable to talk about it, ashamed, not wanting to be seen by friends and neighbours. Mental illness challenges your ability to stay in control of your life, whether you're suffering or caring. Horizons draw in as it becomes easier, perhaps less embarrassing and less painful to stay in, to avoid meeting others, and to keep to a tight-knit circle of people who 'know'. Previously, normal lives yield to a domination by the mental illness, and future security for the whole family – both socially and financially – may become threatened.

Denial is one way of apparently coping. Anxiety and depression are to be expected. Preoccupation with the effects of the illness intrude into all parts of life. That families do survive and individuals do recover from serious mental illness is testament to the resilience of human beings. But for some families the costs become too great – the mental health of carers breaks down, family difficulties can destroy marriages and lose jobs, and people can lead unhappy and unfulfilled lives. A sense of bitterness and hopelessness pervades these families as trust is lost and relationships destroyed.

The emotional needs of the family will differ for each member. In our case, this can be summarised as:

- the two teenage brothers – the peer pressures of having a mentally ill sister; reluctance to bring friends home, to reveal their home life; being ignored as life at home was dominated by their sister's illness

- the parents – grief at the loss created by a long-term mental illness; guilt – parents inevitably blame themselves; anger – with the ill person for their behaviour and the consequences; shame and the stigmatising nature of mental illness in a community

- the grandparents – with their own special perspective; in our case one of the stalwarts of our entire coping strategy was Ann's mum.

Financial pressures can also be created by the time-demands of caring – in our situation, Ann gave up her work. And then there is the emotional strain that will inevitably affect performance at work. If the mentally ill person is the bread-winner, or the main carer for children in a family, then that family's financial viability may be threatened.

Finding support is crucial to carers. A particularly difficult time for us in Mary's illness was her admission to an acute adult ward, and yet we received no psychological support through this process. There's a wide range of experts out there, but you need confidence to handle them, and for many of us the experience can be overwhelmingly difficult. We don't know what to expect, what we should ask for and how to encourage professionals to take us seriously. In our case this was so even though we both worked in a professional capacity within the NHS.

The Importance of Involvement

The pivotal role that informal carers often play in making 'community care' possible is increasingly recognised, carrying with it a right to respect for their own needs. And yet many carers still describe poor experiences of help and support from services. *The National Strategy for Carers* (Department of Health, 1999) and the *National Service Framework for Mental Health* (Department of Health, 1999) give us hope for the future as both highlight the vital role of carers in community care.

When mental health services seek to involve carers/families as part of an overall care package, they often work with them to:

- provide an understanding of the nature of serious mental illness
- engage them in a collaborative therapeutic process
- deal with the impact of the illness on the family
- identify and respond to the needs of individual families.

Psycho-educational Family Intervention also focuses on:

- ongoing relationship problems in the family

- unresolved loss and despair
- problems of coping with psychosis-related behaviour.

The effectiveness of family intervention is well established and should be routinely available. Giving families psychological and educational support reduces relapse rate in schizophrenia, improves family coping and reduces their burden and distress (see various references). Families also act as reservoirs of practical information about the client and their illness; this in turn facilitates a care plan in which the family may be able to play a prominent role in helping supervise medication, understanding and reporting when things begin to go downhill, encouraging participation in rehabilitation programmes, and generally providing love and support.

Looking to the Future

We would like to close with some vision-sharing, in which the person is at the centre of a community-based and fully integrated approach to mental health care recognising roles, responsibilities and rights of families and friends within a whole system of care.

We welcome the demise of institutional care, but would point out that the asylum that Mary nearly became stranded in currently remains open. For many others with long-term mental illness, their current care relies on specialist mental health services offering all-embracing and medicalised care in virtual institutions, lacking simply the bricks and mortar; or for the 'non-compliant' or silent patient sometimes no care at all. The existing service structures and professional boundaries (likened to professionals working in drainpipes!) perpetuate stigmatisation and exclusion of the mentally ill, any distinction between hospital and community becoming increasingly unhelpful.

We expect statutory agencies – primary, social and specialist – to offer truly seamless care, and find unacceptable the current standards of communication, particularly at the interface between primary care and specialist mental health services, leading to poor co-ordination and access. Primary care has an essential and as yet largely undeveloped role. It currently lacks skill, capacity and confidence in treating people with serious and enduring mental illnesses, and yet treats over 90% of *all* people with mental health problems solely in primary care. We need primary care to be able to correlate biological information about an individual within the context of family, culture and social environment and to begin to explain what might previously have been unexplainable through just looking at a biological model. By strengthening primary care with such an approach we must ensure that any model is consistent with the goals, strategy and culture of primary care and not an imported model of specialist mental health care. That is not to say there is no longer a role for specialist care and indeed for facilities that provide a high density of skilled professionals, but these should be available within an integrated service.

Why do we continue to be offered traditional outpatient appointments with all their attached stigma, and the obstacles they raise ('Would you take *your* son or daughter to see a psychiatrist?'). Is it not time to move away from a

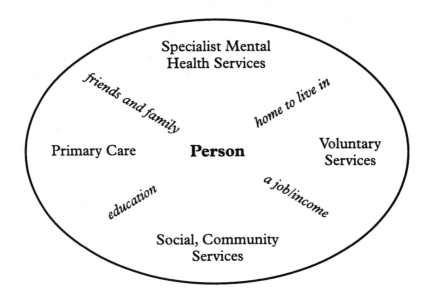

Person-centred Mental Health

purely medical system of care to one founded on simple access to a multidisciplinary team who have the necessary skills and resources to holistically respond to the needs of those with mental illness, and their families, within the communities in which they live?

At the centre of this vision is the recognition that having good mental health depends on more than just health and social care – on things like having friends, a decent home to live in, things to do, the self-esteem you get through having a job.

Within this overall vision of true person-centred care in the community we foresee an ever greater role for family and friends, which must be supported by a fundamental shift in professional attitudes that better acknowledge the family as having a valuable and complimentary role in the care of a person with a serious mental illness.

Paul Boateng, the Minister with responsibility for mental health in 1998, said, in a presentation to the team reviewing mental health legislation:

> *'I am firmly of the opinion that effective service provision can only be delivered if users have played a key part in their design. Carers' views and rights are important and this should also be reflected...'*

Our personal experiences reveal the gulf that lies between that ideal and the reality in our local NHS services. And what chance has an average carer's complaint got compared to people with our professional knowledge? Brian Edwards (Chief Executive of West Midlands Regional Health Authority) stated to a House of Commons Select Committee:

> *'Complaints are jewels to be treasured. They tell us how to do things better next time. If we really believe in quality and have a passion for getting better health services we should search them out vigorously.'*

Finally, can we ask readers to reflect on the way the NHS deals with young people like Mary at such a formative phase.

As a GP, if I practised 1950's cardiology today I would expect to be sued – so how can I and the rest of the NHS justify its current approach to mental health care? It is an indictment of the NHS that 13% of its budget provides the standard of mental health care given to Mary.

References

Department of Health (1999) *Caring about Carers - A National Strategy for Carers.* London: The Stationery Office.

Department of Health (1999) *National Service Framework for Mental Health.* London: The Stationery Office.

For information about family intervention and schizophrenia see also:

Mari, J. & Streiner, D. (1996) The Effects of Family Intervention on Those With Schizophrenia. In: C. Adams, J. Anderson, & M. De Jesus (Eds) *Schizophrenia Module.* Cochrane Database of Systematic Reviews. Available in the Cochrane Library. London: BMJ Publishing.

Falloon, I. & Fadden, G. (1998) *Integrated Community Mental Healthcare: A Community-based Approach.* Cambridge: Cambridge Publications.

Szmukler, G. & Bloch, S. (1997) Family Involvement in the Care of People with Psychoses – an ethical argument. *British Journal of Psychiatry* **171** 401–405.

Furlong, M. & Leggatt, M. (1996) Reconciling the Patient's Right to Confidentiality and the Family's Need to Know. *Australian and New Zealand Journal of Psychiatry* **30** 614–622.

Parts of this chapter are based on an article by the authors in the *British Medical Journal* (March, 1998) **316** 785–786. *The British Medical Journal* has given kind permission for its use here.

Contexts and Frameworks

Release *Jeremy Wooldridge*

I felt as though I didn't have a chance
Of simply picking up where I'd left off.
I felt I had been wrongly diagnosed,
Unjustly punished, waiting for release.

Chapter 5

Legal context across the UK

Margaret Pedler

There are a large number of laws which have an impact on the lives of people with mental health problems. For example, they are affected by social security law which sets down the rules for who can claim Incapacity Benefit or Disability Living Allowance. This chapter is concerned only with three particular areas of the law:

1 *The Mental Health Acts*

2 *The Human Rights Act 1998*

3 *The Disability Discrimination Act 1995*

More detailed treatment of these and other relevant areas of law as they affect England and Wales can be found in *Legal Rights and Mental Health – the Mind Manual* which is available from Mind Publications. Leaflets on mental health law in Scotland and Northern Ireland can be obtained from the Scottish Association for Mental Health and the Northern

Ireland Association for Mental Health. Contact details for all three organisations are given at the end of this chapter.

Section 1: The Mental Health Acts

Purpose

Mental health law is mainly concerned with the circumstances in which a person defined as 'mentally disordered' can have their liberty restricted. With respect to this group of people, it makes lawful acts which would otherwise amount to false imprisonment or assault.

It authorises:

- compulsory detention
- lesser restrictions on liberty, such as requiring residence in a certain place or attendance at places of treatment
- treatment without consent
- control of property and affairs.

Relevant Statutes

There are separate mental health laws for England and Wales, Scotland and Northern Ireland. The key pieces of legislation are:

- *Mental Health Act 1983 (England and Wales)*
- *Mental Health (Scotland) Act 1984*
- *Mental Health (Northern Ireland) Order 1986*
- *Mental Health (Patients in the Community) Act 1995* affecting England, Wales and Scotland.

In addition, the Acts are supplemented by important Codes of Practice which give detailed guidance to registered medical practitioners, managers and staff of hospitals and mental nursing homes and approved social workers (mental health officers in Scotland) on how they should proceed when undertaking duties under the Act. In England and Wales the most recent Code of Practice came into force on 1st April 1999 (Department of Health, 1999[a]).

Definition of 'mental disorder'

All of the Acts listed above only apply to those defined as 'mentally disordered'. This is defined in the *Mental Health Act 1983* (section 1) as meaning: *'mental illness, arrested or incomplete development of mind, psychopathic disorder and any other disorder or disability of mind'*.

Psychopathic disorder is further defined as: *'a persistent disorder or disability of mind (whether or not including significant impairment of intelligence) which results in abnormally aggressive or seriously irresponsible conduct on the part of the person concerned'*.

In the 1983 Act and equivalent Scottish legislation **'mental illness'** is not defined. However, Article 3 (1) of the Northern Ireland Order does define it as *'a state of mind which affects a person's thinking, perceiving, emotion or judgement to the extent that he requires care or medical treatment in his own interests or the interests of other persons'*.

Neither the Scottish nor Northern Ireland definitions include psychopathic disorder and there has recently been some discussion in the context of review of the *Mental Health Act* about removing it in England and Wales. The main argument used by those who favour exclusion is that personality disorders are not treatable and should not therefore be subjected to compulsion under mental health legislation. In their Green Paper published in November 1999 (Department of Health, 1999[b]), the Government say they favour a broad and inclusive definition for England and Wales.

Admission to hospital

The vast majority of people with mental health problems (90% or more) who are in hospital are there as voluntary or informal patients. This means that they are free to leave at any time and have the right to refuse any medical treatment offered. However, concern has been expressed by the Mental

Health Act Commission (a body set up to oversee the operation of the 1983 Act) and others about a group referred to as *'de facto* detained'. These are people who are said to have agreed to be in hospital or to have agreed to accept certain treatment but who in reality have only agreed because they have been given to understand – either implicitly or explicitly – that if they do not consent they will be made to stay anyway or to accept the particular treatment under the procedures in the *Mental Health Act.* The reason this causes concern is because, as is explained below, where the *Mental Health Act* is used, it also includes safeguards for review of treatment or detention. These safeguards are not available to informal patients.

It is important at the outset to distinguish civil detention – where the person detained is not involved with the criminal justice system – and forensic detention where they are.

Civil detention

For civil detention the law in England and Wales is that a person can be detained on the authority of an approved social worker and two doctors:

- for up to 28 days for assessment
  - or assessment followed by treatment if the person is suffering from mental disorder of a nature or degree which warrants detention in hospital and the person needs to be detained *'in the interests of his own health or safety or with a view to the protection of other persons'* (**1983 Act, Section 2**). This section is not renewable

- for up to six months for treatment if:
  - the person is suffering from mental illness, severe mental impairment, psychopathic disorder or mental impairment of a nature or degree which makes it appropriate for him to receive medical treatment in a hospital

- in the case of psychopathic disorder or mental impairment such treatment is likely to alleviate or prevent a deterioration of his condition
- it is necessary for the health or safety of the patient or for the protection of other persons that he should receive such treatment and it cannot be provided unless he is detained under this section (**1983 Act, Section 3**).

This section is renewable for a further six months and then at yearly intervals thereafter.

The position is similar in Scotland and Northern Ireland except that:

- in Scotland, admission for assessment only requires one doctor and longer-term detention has to be agreed by the sheriff's court
- in Northern Ireland, again one doctor only is necessary and admission for assessment is for only seven days initially, although this is renewable.

Forensic detention

For forensic detention in England and Wales a person convicted by either a magistrates' court or Crown Court of offences punishable with imprisonment may be made subject to a hospital order on similar grounds to those for a six- month treatment order set out above (**1983 Act, Section 37**).

In addition the Crown Court may impose a restriction order under **Section 41** if it thinks that *'having regard to the nature of the offence, the antecedents of the offender, and the risk of his committing further offences if set at large, that it is necessary for the protection of the public from serious harm so to do'.*

Where a person is in hospital under **Sections 2, 3 or 37 of the 1983 Act** then they are not free to leave the hospital unless granted leave of absence by their Responsible Medical Officer (RMO). If they go absent without leave then they can be arrested and returned. If they are also subject to a restriction order then any leave also has to be approved by the Home Secretary.

Discharge from hospital

There are various routes by which a person's detention in hospital may come to an end. In England and Wales these are:

- The RMO may discharge them at any time
- Their 'nearest relative' can discharge them unless the RMO bars such discharge by certifying that in his opinion the patient, if discharged, would be *'likely to act in a manner dangerous to other persons or to himself'*. (**1983 Act, Section 25**). A person's nearest relative has to be chosen from a list of relatives laid down in the Act. The detained person cannot choose who this will be
- The detained person can apply for discharge to the managers of the hospital where they are detained. The managers would normally hold a hearing involving the patient and their RMO before deciding whether the criteria for detention were still met
- The detained person or (in certain circumstances) their nearest relative can apply for discharge to a Mental Health Review Tribunal. This Tribunal is made up of a lawyer, a doctor and a lay member who receive reports from the RMO and social services and, following a hearing at which the patient is entitled to be represented, decide whether the criteria for detention continue to apply at the time of the hearing. Where a person is detained for assessment the law requires these hearings to take place very quickly – application has to be made within the first 14 days of detention and the hearing has to be within the next 7 days.

However, where a person is detained under **Section 3** it can often be 8 or 12 weeks after the application that a hearing takes place. This understandably causes frustration and resentment among patients. For detention under **Section 3,** one application can be made to a Tribunal in any period of detention, ie, in the first or second six months or yearly thereafter.

In Northern Ireland the routes for discharge are largely similar although instead of hospital managers appeal is made to the management of the Health and Social Services Board.

In Scotland appeal against short-term detention is to the sheriff court. For longer-term detention there is no appeal for the first six months because detention has been authorised by the sheriff court in the first instance. However, appeal can be made to the court in relation to any renewal.

Treatment

The general position in relation to medical treatment for adults is that it can only be given with consent unless that person lacks the capacity to make treatment decisions – for example, because they have severe learning difficulties or are unconscious. This is the case even if refusal risks permanent injury or premature death. This general rule applies to anyone who is an informal or voluntary patient.

Where a person is detained under the *Mental Health Acts* the position is different. Under this legislation any treatment for mental disorder can be given to detained patients without their consent unless it falls into one of the two categories of treatment for which special rules apply. These two categories are:

1 **psychosurgery** (ie operations on the brain). This can only be given with both consent and a second opinion from a medical practitioner supporting the treatment as beneficial

2 **electro-convulsive therapy (ECT)** and treatment with drugs for more than three months. These can be given without consent but only if a second doctor has agreed with the RMO that the treatment should be given.

This means that even if a person is capable of understanding information about treatment and making a choice they can still have their wishes overridden if they are detained in hospital. **The law behaves as if all detained patients do not have the capacity to make treatment decisions.** Yet research in the United States of America (Appelbaum & Griiso, 1995) has shown that most patients hospitalised with serious mental illness have abilities similar to persons without mental illness for making treatment decisions and that, even where they do not at the time of admission, many of them recover such abilities within two weeks.

It is worth noting that these special rules only apply to treatment for mental disorder although over recent years the courts have stretched the meaning of this term to the limit.

For example, in the case of **B v Croydon Health Authority** (which concerned the feeding by nasogastric tube of a patient with anorexia nervosa) the Court of Appeal held that treatment for a physical disorder arising from a psychiatric disorder was covered. The rationale was that the *Mental Health Act* can be used to sanction treatment which is required first in order that a patient can then be given psychiatric treatment.

This broad interpretation was used in the case of **Tameside and Glossop Acute Services v C.H.** to allow a caesarean section without consent. It was argued that this amounted to part of the treatment for mental disorder because it would prevent a deterioration in the patient's mental condition and enable resumption of strong anti-psychotic medication which had had to be discontinued during the pregnancy.

Compulsion outside hospital

Most of the powers in the *Mental Health Acts* are concerned with treatment in hospital. There are two main exceptions – supervised discharge and guardianship.

Supervised discharge was introduced into England, Wales and Scotland on 1st April 1996 under the *Mental Health (Patients in the Community) Act 1995*. In England and Wales its official title is After-care Under Supervision. In Scotland it is known as a Community Care Order. Under these orders a person who has been detained in hospital for treatment (ie under **Sections 3 or 37 of the 1983 Act**) can have their receipt of aftercare services supervised after they leave hospital. An Order can be imposed if the RMO thinks that there would be a risk of harm to the person themselves or to others if they were not to receive aftercare services and that the Order will help ensure that they do get such services.

Requirements can include:

- living in a certain place
- attending particular places for medical treatment, occupation, education or training
- giving access when required to doctors, social workers and others.

The Order will name both a Community Responsible Medical Officer and a supervisor who will supervise receipt of aftercare services. The supervisor also has the power to 'take and convey' a person to any of the places they are required to be under the conditions in the Order. It is important to note however that once a person has been taken to the relevant place there is no power to require them to stay or force them to take medication. Such powers would only be available if the person was readmitted to hospital under the criteria for admission already set out.

An Order lasts for six months initially although it can then be renewed for a further six months and yearly thereafter. It appears that supervised discharge is not being greatly used.

Guardianship is in many ways similar to supervised discharge although it can be used as an alternative to admission to hospital and the supervisory powers rest with the local authority alone. In addition, there is no power to take and convey.

In the case of both guardianship and supervised discharge the person concerned can apply to a Mental Health Review Tribunal to have the order discharged.

Plans for reform of the law

In October 1998, the Government set up a small team of experts – chaired by Professor Genevra Richardson – to advise them on review of the *1983 Mental Health Act* for

England and Wales. A separate review is taking place in Scotland. The Richardson Committee reported in July 1999 and, in the light of that report, the Government published their own proposals for consultation in November 1999 (DoH, 1999[b]). Key aspects of these proposals are:

- extension of powers of compulsory assessment and treatment to the community

- longer-term powers only to be imposed on the authority of an independent Tribunal

- the right of a detained person to choose a friend or relative to act as their authorised representative.

Pressure for Community Treatment Orders (CTOs) has particularly come from the media and groups concerned about failures in community care particularly where this has lead to deaths. Mind (and others, such as the Manic Depression Fellowship and the Mental Health Foundation) are opposed to such Orders.

Mind's opposition

- CTOs will not be effective. The use of assertive outreach teams and better resourced community services – such as 24-hour crisis teams – are far more likely to engage service users. One of the reasons why people disengage from services now is because they do not help them achieve their life goals and often work against those goals by, for example, prescribing high doses of medication with serious side-effects

- The threat of compulsion will drive users away from services and undermine the trust which should form the basis of any successful therapeutic relationship

- Such Orders are likely to focus on medication to the detriment of other services such as talking treatments, housing, employment and benefits and to be used as an easy option rather than engaging service users in discussion around their own wishes

- It is discriminatory to require people with a diagnosis of mental illness to take medication when no such requirement is imposed on other groups who may present a greater risk to others, such as alcoholics and drug addicts, or a serious risk to themselves, such as diabetics.

The Government are proposing that following assessment it should be open to an Independent Tribunal to impose compulsion in the community covering issues such as place of residence or the nature of proposed care and treatment. It seems likely however that a person who persistently refused to comply with the conditions would probably have to be returned to hospital if the conditions were to continue to be imposed.

Other areas of the *Mental Health Act* where Mind is pressing for reform (Pedler,1999) are:

- service users to have a legal right to assessment and treatment so that they can obtain help early and thus avoid the use of compulsory powers at times of crisis
- a right to free independent advocacy for all those in contact with the mental health system
- greater legal restrictions on the use of ECT, polypharmacy and high doses of drugs
- no compulsory treatment of those who have the capacity to make treatment decisions
- reduction in the overall use of compulsion.

More detailed proposals are expected to be published in the course of 2000.

Section 2: The Human Rights Act 1998

The United Kingdom has long been a signatory to the European Convention on Human Rights (ECHR) which contains a number of rights relevant to those with mental health problems.

Key rights

- The right not to be subjected to torture or to inhuman or degrading treatment or punishment. This was successfully used in 1980 to challenge seclusion conditions in Broadmoor High Security Hospital

- The right not to be deprived of liberty except in accordance with a procedure laid down by law.

The leading case in this area (**Winterwerp** *v* **Netherlands**) has laid down three conditions for the lawful detention of those described in the Convention as being 'of unsound mind'. The decision to detain has to be supported by:

1 objective medical evidence
2 evidence that shows that the patient's disorder is of a kind or degree warranting compulsory confinement
3 the disorder persisting throughout the period of detention.

The importance of this right was highlighted in October 1997 by the case of Stanley Johnson, who was awarded £10,000 for breach of this article. Mr Johnson was a restricted patient who, because of the unavailability of hostel accommodation continued to be detained in Rampton for three and a half years after a Tribunal found he was no longer suffering from a mental illness.

- the right to speedy court proceedings to challenge the lawfulness of detention.

Until now a person wanting to claim a breach of their Convention rights has had to apply to the European Court of Human Rights in Strasbourg, a lengthy and expensive procedure. However under the *Human Rights Act 1998* – which is due to come in to force on 2nd October 2000 – such challenges will be able to be raised directly in UK courts and tribunals. In addition, the courts will be able to make declarations that legislation passed by Parliament is incompatible with the Convention and, in effect, refer the matter back to Parliament for further consideration.

Section 3: The Disability Discrimination Act 1995

The *Disability Discrimination Act 1995* (DDA) – which came into force on 2nd December 1996 – makes it unlawful to discriminate against a 'disabled person' both in employment and in the provision of goods and services. **'Disabled person'** is defined in Section 1 of the Act as a person who has *'a physical or mental impairment which has a substantial and long-term adverse effect on his ability to carry out normal day-to-day activities'*. It therefore applies to people with mental health problems – not just those with physical disabilities.

Under the Act it is unlawful for any employer of 15 or more people, for all providers of goods and services, and for providers of land, property and accommodation to treat a disabled person less favourably than they treat or would treat other people, unless they can justify their behaviour.

In addition, employers have a duty to make adjustments to the working environment or working arrangements to accommodate any substantial disadvantage experienced by a disabled person. A refusal or failure to do so without justification will amount to discrimination. From October 1999, service providers have had to take reasonable steps to:

- change practices, policies or procedures which make it impossible or unreasonably difficult for disabled people to use a service

- provide auxiliary aids or services which would enable disabled people to use a service

- overcome physical barriers by providing a service by a reasonable alternative method.

From 2004 service providers will have to take reasonable steps to remove, alter or provide reasonable means of avoiding physical features that make it impossible or unreasonably difficult for disabled people to use a service.

This Act has already made a difference to some people with mental health problems. For example, in Scotland in 1997, a woman with a diagnosis of bi-polar affective disorder who was dismissed successfully claimed unfair dismissal. In

1999, a woman was awarded £7,000 by a Tribunal after she was sacked because agoraphobia stopped her travelling.

However, the Act also has many limitations. It did not create a body to publicise the Act and help people take cases such as the Equal Opportunities Commission for sex discrimination and the Commission for Racial Equality for race discrimination. The definition of 'disabled person' also does not cover many of those with mental health problems who do experience discrimination. For example, a person who suffered from severe depression for six months and was sacked, or who later found it impossible to get a job because of this would not fall within the definition.

Following strong lobbying by the disability movement the Government have recognised these limitations. They have already passed legislation to set up a Disability Rights Commission from April 2000 which will have power to take up cases. In addition they have appointed a Disability Rights Task Force which is looking at how to amend the DDA to secure comprehensive and enforceable civil rights for disabled people. The Task Force is due to report to Ministers towards the end of 1999.

Free leaflets on the Disability Discrimination Act are available from Disability on the Agenda, FREEPOST, Bristol, BS38 7DE. Tel: 0345 622633 (textphone 0345 622644).

Addresses

Mind
15-19 Broadway
Stratford
London E15 4BQ
Tel: 020 8519 2122

Leaflets on mental health law in Scotland and Northern Ireland can be obtained from the Scottish Association for Mental Health and the Northern Ireland Association for Mental Health.

Scottish Association for Mental Health (SAMH)
Cumbrae House
15 Carlton Court
Glasgow G5 9JB
Tel: 0141 568 7000

Northern Ireland Association for Mental Health (NIAMH)
80 University Street
Belfast BT7 1HE
Tel: 01232 328474

Case references

B v Croydon Health Authority [1995] 1 All England Reports 683.

Tameside and Glossop Acute Services v C.H. [1996] Family Law Reports 762.

Winterwerp v Netherlands [1979] European Human Rights Reports **2** 387.

References

Appelbaum, P. S. & Griiso, T. (1995) The MacArthur Treatment Competence Study: 1 Mental Illness and Competence to Consent to Treatment. In: *Law and Human Behaviour* **19** 105–126.

Department of Health (1999a) *Code of Practice Mental Health Act 1983.* London: The Stationery Office.

Mind (1996) *Legal Rights and Mental Health - the Mind Manual.* London: Mind Publications.

Department of Health (1999b) *Reform of the Mental Health Act 1983 - Proposals for Consultation.* London: The Stationery Office.

Pedler, M. (1999) *Mind the Law - Mind's Evidence to the Government's Mental Health Act Review Team.* London: Mind Publications.

**From the series "New Sussex Hospital" Trap Door: What can it be, this mystery?
A square amidst conformity**   *Olive M.*

New Sussex Hospital
Leila Atherton

Looking to the Future © Pavilion Publishing/Mental Health Foundation, 2000

Chapter 6

Individual care planning in the UK

Steve Morgan & Su Akbar-Khan

Care planning is a process whereby identified needs and wants are translated into real actions. For people experiencing severe and enduring mental health problems, needs and wants are generally complex, covering health and social care issues, including housing, finances and personally meaningful occupation or activity.

Care planning is a continuous process of developing and reviewing actions, stated as achievable tasks, allocated responsibilities and agreed timescales. In this way, it is a practical function in the here and now, both enabling agreement of goals for the future, and the monitoring of past achievements and progress.

Whilst it is commonly seen as a 'professional' activity, it is only truly reflective of individual needs if the service user is central to the process. Most health and social care professionals see it as an element of a cyclical process, involving 'assessment - care planning - active intervention - evaluation'. However, advocacy and service-user involvement has helped support a shift to a 'client-centred, needs-led approach' (Morgan, 1993). The emphasis is firmly on the individual service user as an active partner at the centre of the care planning process not just as the recipient of care from the professionals.

Guidance and Legislation

At a national level (England and Wales), the concept of individual care planning is enshrined in the legislative context of Section 117 of the *1983 Mental Health Act*, and *The Mental Health (Patients in the Community) Act 1995,* and in equivalent legislation in Northern Ireland and Scotland. Implementation of Department of Health guidance has taken the form of the Care Programme Approach (CPA) in England and Scotland (1991 and 1992 respectively); whereas in Northern Ireland and Wales the term CPA is not used, but procedures to enable multidisciplinary care planning and review follow similar principles of good practice.

At the local level, caution is recommended when considering the implementation of some of the above directives. The CPA in particular, is much more responsive to local interpretations of population need and resource configurations. In practice, it is seen much more as an administration arrangement, characterised by bureaucracy and paperwork, rather than a clinical function governing efficient use of resources. The 'politics and personalities' can often exert more influence than the concept of service-user needs and wants.

Broad Principles

Whether adopting the CPA or not, there is a general consensus that the framework of good practice should include:

- health and social care needs-assessment
- an explicit care plan with named care providers

- a nominated, and agreed, care co-ordinator
- regular care-review meetings.

  (DoH, 1995; Social Work Services Inspectorate for Scotland, 1998; NHS Executive South Thames, 1998)

Good practice in assessment and care planning must be based on a foundation of engaged, trusting working relationships, between an individual service user and service provider. It also requires that the development of positive and constructive action plans be based upon a consideration of service-user strengths, abilities and aspirations, not just identified problems (Morgan, 1996; Kisthardt, 1992).

Principles into Practice

Good quality, functional care plans are not simply pieces of paper that gather dust in a file. They represent the accumulated discussions between the service user and relevant care provider(s). The discussions will take the form of conversations, formal assessments, disagreements, negotiations and decisions, made in the course of direct/indirect client–service and service–service contacts. The plan is a dynamic set of agreements, preferably signed and dated by the relevant parties, to be used as a guide for the actions to be completed during the next phase of service contacts.

Plans that offer a genuine guide to action should generally be copied to all relevant people involved. They may perform the function of a quasi-legal contract, documenting agreed actions between parties. They can act as reminders of the responsibilities that were signed up to at the last review meeting.

However, in reality, the all-important service users and significant carers do not appear as well informed about the process as we would ideally wish them to be (Allen, 1998; Phillips, 1998). Which begs a number of questions: are some care plans simply seen as administrative duties to be processed and filed, at the specified regulation time intervals?

Do practitioners give sufficient explanation and information to service users and carers, for example, by using available information leaflets? Or does this area of work fall victim to misguided assumptions and forgetfulness, within the burden of heavy workloads?

A Multi-agency Function

Effective planning of individualised care packages may be a routine function in simple arrangements where a service user is in contact with only one practitioner for their identified needs. However, more frequently it is a complex arrangement of multidisciplinary and multi-agency involvement, to meet a broad-ranging set of needs and wants.

The 'psychiatric community' is a very complex place. Statutory sector services are distributed between health and social care agencies. Housing and welfare rights are administered through entirely different agencies; and the voluntary sector is a patchwork of flexible and creative groups of people, developing services in relation to a dynamic mix of locally identified need and complex funding arrangements.

No single agency or profession holds a monopoly on the skills or resources for meeting the challenging range of individual needs. Yet the common picture requires a service user experiencing the distress and chaos of a mental health problem, to relate to a potentially confusing range of agencies. Each agency may identify its own keyworker, and draw up its own action plan with the individual. The recipe is frequently unco-ordinated, lacking any clarity of communication between the separate functions of the different workers and agencies.

The key to effective care planning requires collaborative joint working between all agencies involved in the delivery of care with the individual service user. This requires clear lines of communication, whilst also respecting the principle of client confidentiality; and the acceptance of responsibility by individual workers to co-ordinate the various inputs to the total care plan.

The Department of Health (1995) reflects the sensitivity of this issue, by recognising that

'....*the sharing of relevant information is vital if multidisciplinary and inter-agency care is to function effectively. At the same time, mentally ill people are entitled to the same confidential handling of information about their health or social care as any other patient or client'.*

Confidentiality poses a philosophical dilemma that has yet to be resolved to the satisfaction of all interested parties. The consequences of not passing on information are all too evident, particularly in the rare, but highly publicised, incidents of homicide (Ritchie *et al,* 1994). Anecdotally, experience suggests that service users rarely object on the basis of confidentiality, if they trust their worker(s) to explain to them to *whom* the information is being passed, and for what purposes. The sharing of information may then be seen to be in the service user's interests. Conversely, where trust is not sufficiently established, and explanations are less forthcoming, there is a greater potential for suspicion, due to a lack of clear boundaries on information-sharing. In this latter case, objections may be raised more readily.

Care Co-ordination

The care plan should reflect the responsibilities and actions of all relevant people involved in the care, treatment and support of the individual service user. Reports of inquiries into incidents of risk frequently highlight that co-ordination of all components of the care package was either lacking or non-existent (Sheppard, 1996). The co-ordination function needs to be an explicit responsibility, designated to the 'identified keyworker', who will usually be the best placed person to draw up and monitor the care plan. The Department of Health (1995) recognises the keyworker role to be a significant component of effective care planning, requiring the nomination of a person, with consideration to client needs and practitioner workload. Sufficient time needs to be available to fulfil the considerable practical requirements of the co-ordination function; and keyworkers/care co-ordinators from whatever background, need adequate training and support to perform the tasks.

Standards for Care Co-Ordination

The following list of questions is designed as a guide to the requirements for implementing effective care co-ordination, which will subsequently underpin individualised care planning.

1 Service-level responsibility

- Do you have a system for prioritising which are the complex cases requiring the most detailed discussions?

- Are 'realistic' expectations placed on the individuals, the team, and the process itself, within the available resources and priorities?

- What support will be offered to staff who followed good practice guidelines, but subsequent outcomes were still negative?

2 Keyworker/care co-ordinator responsibility

- How are the sources of information to be collected, collated and processed into a useful assessment, on which to base the decisions and plans?

- How will the decisions be recorded, and communicated to the relevant people?

- Has the keyworker/care co-ordinator been invested with the power and authority to control the whole process; or does the consultant psychiatrist wield a 'professional' authority over the proceedings?

- Has the keyworker/care co-ordinator been invested with the necessary authority, and support, to monitor the progress of the plan through to the next review meeting?

3 Organisation of meetings

- How was the venue determined?

- How will the person chairing the meeting be supported and trained to perform the function effectively?

- Who will be taking the minutes of the meeting?

- How do you allocate sufficient time for complex meetings, to ensure discussion of priority issues, and for formulating achievable plans?

4 Participation in meetings

- Is the service user present? If not, what mechanisms are in place to ensure their needs and wishes take priority? For example, how could the meeting be split, either into sub-meetings on the day, or into separate meetings at different times, to ensure the service user's wishes and concerns can be adequately accommodated?

- Are the relevant carers present and/or involved?

- What considerations are being made to support the active involvement of general practitioners in the process?

- How will the views be represented of those workers/agencies who are involved but are unable to attend?

- How do you ensure that persistent non-attendance cannot be used as a mechanism for avoiding allocation of work and responsibilities?

- How will the participants consider 'potential future crises', and share ideas for responding to them within the constraints of local resources, and collective 'creativity'?

Audit

Encouraging care plans to be effective and functional will require regular feedback of the outcomes to the service user, carers, involved workers from all agencies, and service managers. The process of evaluation, through review meetings, will offer some reflection of whether the process is working effectively. But, for paperwork to be usable, it will require more constant use and feedback through progress against the stated goals and responsibilities. The fears are that managerial audit will be seen as a method of checking up on people in a negative way, with the sinister potential for cutting resources. Whether this situation is real or perceived, will largely depend on the organisational culture that prevails within an area service.

Audit feedback on the quality and utility of care plans may also facilitate the dissemination of good practice, and support the appropriate level of uniformity of the process across the service.

Challenges Ahead

Care planning is frequently seen as the paperwork representation of an office-based administrative process. It needs to be seen in a more positive light by practitioners, as the recording of a practical and dynamic series of inter-relationships, between all people involved in the care and support of the individual service user (Sanderson *et al,* 1997).

Communication across agencies and disciplines often presents difficulties, through different priorities and protocols. The issue of overlap with social services care-management responsibilities cannot be under-emphasised. This is only one of the many points that can confuse the debate as to who should be the overall 'care co-ordinator/keyworker'.

Involvement of GPs, and primary care in general, requires particular attention. They play a significant part in the care, treatment and support of many people experiencing severe and enduring mental health problems. Yet, their priorities and working practices frequently diverge from the traditional processes of the specialist mental health services, such as the CPA (NHS Executive South Thames, 1998).

Active listening to the service user, and promoting attention to the importance of strengths and abilities, will offer opportunities for greater service-user involvement in the whole process (Morgan, 1996).

Effective networking and co-ordination will help to avoid the frustrations of resource duplication. This is particularly important in relation to the issue of ensuring realistic workloads to manage the considerable time required to co-ordinate information, from multiple sources, into a coherent plan.

This chapter has focused exclusively on the needs of the service user within the process of care planning. Acknowledgement needs to be made to the statutory right of carers to their own independent needs assessment, particularly through social services care-management procedures. This will present a significant challenge to care co-ordination and planning in situations where the carer's needs are in conflict with the service user's needs.

References

Allen, C. (1998) The Care Programme Approach: The Experiences and Views of Carers. *Mental Health Care* **1** (5) 160–162.

Department of Health (1995) *The Health of the Nation, Building Bridges: A Guide to Arrangements For Inter-agency Working for the Care and Protection of Severely Mentally Ill People.* London: DoH.

Kisthardt, W. E. (1992) The Strengths Model of Case Management: The Principles and Functions of a Helping Partnership with Persons with Persistent Mental Illness. In: D. Saleeby (Ed) *A Strengths Perspective for Social Work Practice*, pp59–83. New York: Longman.

Morgan, S. (1993) *Community Mental Health: Practical Approaches to Long-term Problems.* Cheltenham: Stanley Thornes.

Morgan, S. (1996) *Helping Relationships in Mental Health.* Cheltenham: Stanley Thornes.

NHS Executive South Thames (1998) *Engaging Primary Care in the Care Programme Approach: an Evaluation.* London: Health Care Evaluation Unit and NHS Executive.

Phillips, P. (1998) The Care Programme Approach: The Views and Experiences of Service Users. *Mental Health Care* **1** (5) 166–168.

Ritchie, J., Dick, D. & Lingham, R. (1994) *The Report of the Inquiry into the Care and Treatment of Christopher Clunis.* London: The Stationery Office.

Sanderson, H., Kennedy, J., Ritchie, P. & Goodwin, G. (1997) *People, Plans and Possibilities: Exploring Person-centred Planning.* Edinburgh: SHS.

Sheppard, D. (1996) *Learning the Lessons.* 2nd Edn. London: Zito Trust.

Social Work Services Inspectorate for Scotland (1998) *Implementing the Care Programme Approach: Results of a Joint Survey.* Edinburgh: SWSI.

Phobia

'Don't go near that depressed person'
I hear you say
'He will take the sunlight out of your life
And replace it with brooding darkness.'
'Don't trust his moodswings:
One minute up
next minute down
Brimming with enthusiasm
Then sinking into apathy.'

'I say I'm just trying to be real.'

Old fucked up
old messed up
He will bring you down
Laugh at him,
Tell him he's no good.
You say he's aggressive
you learn to fear
But outside in the competitive world
There is a real war.

Who would love a depressed person?
They say he's a terrible bore
But deep in his heart
He wants to share.
'No, I don't like this darkness
Any more than you do
I would like to share a little sunlight
on a magic island made for two.'

Old misery guts
Antisocial
Likes being alone
Do you listen to his words
When he tries to talk to you?

Funny boy
Mental boy
Always
a miss with the girls
Turn him into a monster
Ignore his fears...

'But I prefer my real face
To any mask
The paint runs when it rains
And masks blow away in the wind.'
Mood controlling drugs
Do they work?
Do they hurt?
'Do I care about being labelled mad?
Can I express myself?'

'Don't trust a depressed person'
I hear you say
Leave him in his corner
To fade away.
'But a sunbeam danced around the room
Just the other day.
We could have danced around the room together
If the world was a more receptive place.'

Frank Bangay, April 1997

Chapter 7

Risk and safety

Steve Morgan

'My son the psycho...'

'Released from hospital to kill...'

'Schizophrenic stalked victim...'

I do not know if these headlines have really appeared in print, but it is most disturbing just how familiar they look and sound. Without doubt, one of the most overwhelming issues confronting contemporary community mental health, is its portrayal in the media. The focus is almost entirely on violence and homicides perpetrated by people experiencing mental health problems living in the community.

The impact is far reaching; initially influencing public fears for their own safety, which in turn shapes government rhetoric and legislation. The sharp impact is felt by mental health services charged with implementing directives to halt the so-called failure of the community care policy. Ultimately, this chain of events arrives at the most important interface – the individual service user and the service providers. Users of services suffer the stigma of having mental health problems deepened by the additional labels of 'risk' and 'dangerous'; and service practitioners turn to more defensive practices for fear of being blamed and scape-goated for failure.

The Evidence

Following the above line of argument, for such a wide-ranging policy as community care to have failed, there must be an increasing and substantial proportion of homicides committed by the population defined as having mental health problems. The Zito Trust has published its report *Learning the Lessons* (Sheppard, 1996) which outlines the findings and recommendations of public inquiries into such homicides. The consistent failure of mental health services to adequately assess the risk, and to subsequently communicate and co-ordinate the management of the risk, suggests that much work needs to be done to raise standards of care to promote greater safety.

Whilst acknowledging the importance of such lessons, we still need to see the problem in its fuller context. Every homicide is a tragedy, with a widespread impact on people closely involved (relatives, friends, service users and practitioners alike), which should not be diminished in any way. Yet, the latest analysis of homicides between 1957 and 1995 leads us to very different conclusions than those previously suggested by a failed policy (Taylor & Gunn, 1999).

Annual figures suggest an average of 36 homicides a year are committed by people diagnosed as having a mental illness (with a range of between 19 and 58 people in a year across this time). Of these figures, a very small proportion of the victims were complete strangers. Furthermore, analysis in relation to the forensic statistics for the general population suggests that the rate of homicides committed by people with mental illness remains relatively static, but is a diminishing proportion of the total.

Put into further perspective, Taylor and Gunn remind us that the police record approximately 600–700 homicides per year in England and Wales, with a further 300 killings resulting from drink/drug driving offences, and 3500-4000 deaths recorded as road accidents. Therefore, formulating a national policy for mental health on the tragic actions of 36 people would be equitable to abolishing private motoring because of the 4000 road deaths. **Statistically, there is a greater chance of winning the National Lottery than being killed by a person with a mental illness.** However, the authors do acknowledge a duty on mental health services to do everything possible to reduce this small figure even further.

The Meaning of Risk

'Risk is the likelihood of an identified behaviour occurring in response to changing personal circumstances. The outcomes are more frequently harmful to self or others, though occasionally they may have a beneficial aim in pursuit of a positive change.'

(Morgan, 1998a)

This definition broadens the field of interest beyond issues of aggression and violence, to incorporate **other categories of risk** such as:

- suicide
- self harm
- severe self-neglect

as recognised by the introduction of supervision registers (NHS Executive, 1994). The Department of Health and Royal College of Psychiatrists have supported a major national study into suicides and homicides, which clearly reports suicides to be statistically more significant than homicide (Appleby, 1997). So, one challenge for mental health services is to maintain a focus on all of the relevant issues, not just those that receive most media attention.

This definition also reflects upon other challenges posed by the concept of risk; namely, an awareness of the 'context' of behavioural changes, not just the outcomes; and the potential for 'positive risk-taking', not just defensive practice to restrict potentially harmful results.

Service Users' Perspectives

The list of categories of risk (on page xx) is far from exhaustive, and one of the major omissions is 'exploitation'. Most of the literature on risk is written from the perspective of the service user as 'perpetrator'; whether posing a risk to self, or a risk to others. Very little consideration is given to the service user's more frequent experiences of risk – that of 'victim'.

Exploitation is of itself a very narrow category in relation to the catalogue of experiences service users encounter as victims. These victim experiences range from physical to financial, self-worth to social exclusion, and a litany of losses from housing to human rights. The perpetrators may range from the public at large to the neighbours in the local community, and from family to mental health workers. The challenge for all mental health workers is one of incorporating the service user's own real and perceived experiences of risk within the comprehensive strategies of assessment and management, placing the service user in their rightful position – at the centre of the whole process, not simply as recipient of the practitioner's prescriptions and interventions.

Issues of Risk Assessment

The assessment of risk has gained prominence in recent years, having been highlighted as a particular service failing by influential reports (Ritchie *et al,* 1994).

However, the literature and research into risk has identified some common themes, which have significant bearing on our abilities in this field; these are that:

1   incidents of risk are rare - requiring us to make predictions on limited experience (Duggan, 1997)

2   mental illnesses are significant factors when assessing the potential for risk (Duggan, 1997; Appleby, 1997)

3   prediction is an uncertain activity that we achieve successfully in only a minority of attempts (Rose, 1998).

The most significant research into the practice of risk assessment in mental health is the MacArthur Risk Assessment Study in the US (Steadman *et al*, 1994). This is a multi-site longitudinal study of approximately 1000 people. Its primary purpose is to inform a new generation of comprehensive risk-assessment tools, based on more robust risk-factor analysis, and an examination of how the results can be translated into routine clinical practice through training programmes. Its current claims are to have supported improvements in predictive ability through a more rigorous investigation of researched risk factors.

However, the greater reliance in the US on statistical enumeration of risk, through weighted indicators and rating scales receives scepticism in UK clinical practice. Whilst acknowledging the need for standardised approaches to risk assessment, there remains a strong support for the importance of 'clinical judgement' in the individual relationships between service users and practitioners. The issue is one of combining the individuality of the circumstances, with the need to standardise the means of accessing and communicating information between the relevant people involved in the care plan and risk-management plan.

Further issues are those of **frequency** and **timescale**. As with all other aspects of assessment, risk assessment is a continuous process that can fluctuate very rapidly. We are required, alongside our predictions of what risks may occur, to suggest a timescale for the accuracy of such statements; for example, a high risk of suicide will remain until (specified) situations change. Realistic expectations need to be attached to such demands for predictive statements as human nature is a very unpredictable element at the best of times. One hundred per cent accuracy, and associated risk elimination, are not possible to achieve. But we can improve our assessments by more comprehensively understanding the historical and contextual circumstances in which a person is more prone to behave in a 'risky' manner (Morgan, 1998a).

Issues of Risk Management

Risk management receives far less attention in the research and literature than risk assessment. Essentially, it is the actions taken, and responsibilities assumed, by all people identified in the plan, within the local implementation of national guidance and legislation (Morgan & Hemming, 1999). It is important to view the assessment and management of risk as two inter-related concepts – the identification of risk must lead onto active responses, through a logical process of collective decision-making. Similarly, the management of risks will provide valuable information for the ongoing process of assessment (Morgan, 1998b).

The management of risk in the UK needs to be seen within the broad context of mental health legislation and guidance. The Care Programme Approach (CPA), in England and Scotland (Multidisciplinary Care Planning in Wales), forms the administrative guidelines for multi-agency care co-ordination. Failures of care co-ordination are one of the most frequent findings from the public inquiries into incidents of risk (Sheppard, 1996). Furthermore, the introduction of supervision registers in England (NHS Executive, 1994), and subsequent supervised discharge in 1996, specifically focuses on risk as a definition of highest priority for care co-ordination.

Risk management should also be seen as an important element of community mental-health team operational policy and daily practice. This focus should ensure attention is given to individual clinical practice within the context of team resources and peer supervision as well as addressing issues of safety for all people involved in the management of risk.

There can be no substitute for developing trusting working relationships between service users and their service providers. To this end, risk management should be seen first and foremost as a collaborative function. Prevention is the desired aim of everyone, and can be enhanced through engaging in meaningful dialogue about all potential risks, to and from the service user. However, Morgan and Hemming (1999) suggest that in the event of risks occurring, there are a range of strategies that need to be considered for managing the risks during and after the event, always with a view to minimising the impact of the outcomes for all involved. The recurrent consideration in the UK mental health services is of the need for some form of compulsory powers to treat people in the community. The opponents of Community Treatment Orders (CTOs) argue that powers already exist, and any strengthening of the position will be limited to enforcement of medication. Morgan and Hemming suggest that if stronger powers are to be legislated, medication alone is not an effective basis for collaborative risk management. CTOs should be seen more as an imposition on the *service* rather than the individual service user – requiring that a hard-to-engage individual who presents potential risks should be offered a range of service options, not solely an approach based on compulsory medication backed by a threat of involuntary detention. Risks will be likely to increase if people disengage from services; but, many people disengage on the basis that the services are neither relevant, understanding or responsive to their needs.

Care *v* Control

Rose (1998) offers a discussion that challenges us to look more critically at the way risk has come to dominate the debate about mental health clinical practice. He suggests that the institutions developed to replace the old long-stay hospitals are defined more by the need for 'security' than considerations for 'care and therapy'. The very structure of the mental health system is shaped by an imperative to manage risk, and the same considerations become the central professional obligation for all practitioners. Principally, Rose suggests that 'risk-thinking' now dominates mental health practice in a way that it didn't ten years ago. Judgements of risk are no longer the prerogative of the forensic psychiatrist assessing dangerousness; now all practitioners assessing personal and family history, housing suitability, use of alcohol or drugs, do so within the expressed remit of assigning a level of risk.

Accountability and Responsibility

One of the most significant repercussions of this 'risk-thinking' is the sense of an associated culture of blame. Society now appears to be far less tolerant of any inability to manage the extreme, the rare, and the unpredictable. When something goes wrong, blame needs to be apportioned. Whilst this is not solely applied to the field of mental health, it is a prominent target, led by the media scrutiny of any flaw that can be levelled at the policy of community care.

Rose (1998) recognises a negative effect of this scapegoating is the proliferation of 'defensive practice', based firstly on covering your back before considering the real needs of the service user.

Consideration is increasingly given to what responsibilities should be assumed of the mental health staff working with users presenting with high risks. What should service providers be held accountable for? The culture of blame is fuelled by a sense that individuals will be named on the CPA documentation, with the resulting blame being easily attached to psychiatrist and keyworker.

Morgan (1998a) suggests that individual practitioners can reasonably be expected to accept responsibility for the professional standards of conduct set out by their professional body, and for the keyworker role within the local implementation of the guidance and legislation. However, there are also shared responsibilities for information-sharing, decision-making and care planning that belong with the collective 'team'. The 'organisation' also holds responsibilities, for ensuring that its staff are adequately supported and resourced to perform the duties expected of them, and to provide adequate guidance through a risk policy.

Challenges Ahead

In addition to the issues outlined throughout this chapter, risk poses a number of other challenges for contemporary mental health services:

- The whole concept of risk needs to be seen within the context of comprehensive mental health service provision – it is the mental health business, with risk as an important facet, not the other way around

- The context is one of integrated teams working in a multidisciplinary, multi-skilled, multi-agency network – such effective communication and co-ordination are essential – not simply desired options

- The developments in the legislative and legal frameworks need to support service-user involvement in all issues of mental health delivery, including risk

- Positive risk-taking needs to be clearly defined, and encouraged as a routine aspect of creative, engaged working relationships. It will support risk-prevention strategies, not create more incidents

- The issues of responsibility and support for people labelled as 'personality disordered' need to be more clearly defined between the mental health and criminal justice systems. It will not be a blanket either-or responsibility; both systems need to work on clear guidelines, not as opponents in a tennis match.

Perhaps the most difficult challenge will be a need to influence the media representation of mental health issues, particularly in the reporting of risk. This is a collective responsibility shared by all stakeholders, from service users to service practitioners, from managers to government departments.

References

Appleby, L. (1997) *National Confidential Inquiry into Suicide and Homicide by People with Mental Illness.* London: The Stationery Office.

Duggan, C. (Ed) (1997) Assessing risk in the mentally disordered. *British Journal of Psychiatry* **170** (32).

Morgan, S. (1998a) *Assessing and Managing Risk: A Trainers Manual and Practitioner Handbook.* Brighton: Sainsbury Centre for Mental Health/Pavilion Publishing.

Morgan, S. (1998b) The Assessment and Management of Risk. In: C. Brooker & J. Repper (Eds) *Serious Mental Health Problems in the Community - Policy, Practice and Research* pp265-290. London: Bailliere Tindall.

Morgan, S. & Hemming, M. (1999) Risk Management and Community Treatment Orders. *Mental Health Care* (in press).

NHS Executive (1994) Introduction of Supervision Registers for Mentally Ill People from 1 April 1994. *HSG* **5** (94). London: Department of Health.

Ritchie, J. H., Dick, D. & Lingham, R. (1994) *The Report of the Inquiry into the Care and Treatment of Christopher Clunis.* London: The Stationery Office.

Rose, N. (1998) Living Dangerously: Risk-thinking and Risk Management in Mental Health Care. *Mental Health Care* **1** (8) 263–266.

Sheppard, D. (1996) *Learning the Lessons.* 2nd Edn. London: Zito Trust.

Steadman, H. J., Monahan, J. & Appelbaum, P. S. (1994) Designing a New Generation of Risk Assessment Research. In: J. Monahan & H. J. Steadman (Eds) *Violence and Mental Disorder: Developments in Risk Assessment.* Chicago: University of Chicago Press.

Taylor, P. J. & Gunn, J. (1999) Homicides by People With Mental Illness: Myth and Reality. *British Journal of Psychiatry* **174** 9–14.

Chapter 8

Anti-racist practice in mental health assessment

Loretta Fuller

The arena of race, mental health and illness has been highlighted on the agenda of the Black community and others, for several years. More recent misjustices and little evidence of change within practice in the psychiatric arena have resulted in a call for action that demands more than simply further rhetoric of the plight of the disadvantaged, but also a physical change to what is considered an oppressive institution.

One particular case was noted as significant by the Black community, the community-at-large and government agencies: an incident took place in Rackhams in Birmingham in the mid-80s, in which a Black client who had disengaged from mental health services attacked several women with a knife. The incident was extensively reported in the press at the time and was the subject of a television documentary. Amongst other things, this case highlighted issues of relationship with services and consequent risks. It became the preceptor to the actual take-up of introducing services that had a particular focus on the African Caribbean group. It also instigated further examination into promoting better service provision, with a recognised need to improve the accuracy and quality of assessments. This would be done through collaboration with the community.

The Frantz Fanon Centre for Mental Health was developed following these expressed concerns from the Black community, and from statutory and non-statutory agencies who had a particular interest and desire to change the experience of Black people who came into contact with psychiatric services.

The Centre comprises the following six specific components designed to target the key areas in relation to Black people's experience in psychiatry and correlating agencies that further compound the antecedents to mental ill health:

1 outreach and community support
2 crisis and residential support
3 training, employment and vocational team
4 psychotherapy and counselling
5 children, young adults and families
6 advocacy.

The concerns of the Centre are to impact in the following areas:

- the over-representation of Black people in psychiatry, with particular emphasis in the 'hard end' of services
- the high level of admissions under compulsion of sections of the *Mental Health Act 1983*
- the misdiagnosis of schizophrenia and psychosis
- the overuse of medication as a form of treatment
- limited access to psychotherapy and counselling.

The aim of the Frantz Fanon Centre is to impact on the negativity of the experience, and to address the need to provide a more accurate and effective way of assessing the presenting situation. This should result in determining a more positive and productive pathway for the individual and will influence what s/he will utilise and be supported with along the way.

Assessment of Risk, Race and Mental Health

The concept of risk and its association with race is significant in the assessment of Black people and their presentation to the psychiatric arena.

The notion of 'risk to others' had become more prevalent and received a great amount of media attention as a consequence of particular tragedies that involved those who:

- were experiencing psychiatric difficulties

- were being failed by psychiatric services

- for various reasons, were not in a process of continuous, meaningful engagement.

The importance of examining the significance between this and the experience of Black people who have contact with services is to incorporate the processes that predispose their clinical encounter. It has been argued that there could be a circuitous process that involves a number of agencies, which applies labels of abnormality and have the power to remove an individual from society (Browne, Francis & Crowe, 1993).

The assessment of risk has tended to become engrossed with the concept of 'dangerousness' and safety to the public and others.

The notion of violence is also closely associated with Black males and in examining relationships with Black people who come into contact with services; this notion has also been introduced and presented as if it were a 'cultural norm'.

The reality is that the services present a greater risk to Black people who come into contact with them, because the inaccuracies of assessment can lead them onto a more negative pathway that results in loss of freedom, denial of self, and for some, the ultimate – death.

The analysis of behaviour and symptoms of mental ill health amongst Black people is often influenced by powerful stereotypes. This would include assessment outcomes that describe it to be normal for Black people to express emotion in a loud and aggressive manner; or that Black people are very physical in their expression and that they speak with a foreign dialect when under stress, which renders communication difficult. However, these same observations tend to be presented as evidence that the client is 'difficult to engage' and 'potentially violent and aggressive'.

There have been numerous cases that outline that non-compliance with the care plan that has been formulated on the basis of the assessment has been used as an indicator to support the need for a more intensive or controlling level of care. This is usually presented as increased medication, increased monitoring and hospitalisation. Terms such as 'difficult to engage' or 'refusal to comply' have become the labels that compound the Black individual's experience of psychiatry. The services somehow view this as symptomatic of relapse and enduring mental illness.

Problems With Conventional Assertive Outreach and Traditional Assessment Models

The response of Western psychiatric services to improve the outcomes for the individual – who, it is stated, requires a more intensive level of support – has been to introduce assertive outreach teams. Models, primarily developed in the USA, were adopted for use in Britain shortly after a series of incidents that involved clients who had come into contact with psychiatric services and the general public. The aim is to improve and provide effective and appropriate services to people who have been described as 'difficult to engage' and who have no desire to comply with traditional mental health services.

It has been stated that the majority of Black people who come into contact with the psychiatric services tend to have a higher degree of need and do not desire to comply with mental health services (Commander *et al*, 1997).

Therefore, the advent of traditional assertive outreach services has implications for individuals from the African Caribbean Diaspora who experience mental health problems and come into contact with their services.

Examination of the criteria for assertive outreach services gives a sound example of how an analysis of the outcome of the individual's initial contact with services can result in accessing this 'hard end' of psychiatric care provision.

Criteria for assertive outreach provision

- clients who lose contact with services following discharge from hospital
- clients who fail to continue taking medication
- clients who come back into contact with services in a compulsive manner due to relapse of psychiatric symptoms and who are stated to require hospital admission
- clients with a history of violence-related experiences
- clients who present with a degree of risk
- clients who have had contact with forensic services

These particular indicators are analogous to descriptions of Black people and their experience of psychiatry. It has become more evident as a likely outcome to the process that brings Black people onto a particular pathway of psychiatric care provision when they initially access psychiatric services.

For those individuals who are on the continuum of care that enables access to assertive outreach services, there is an already-achieved history conducive to the requirements for admission to this element of psychiatric community support. There will be evidence to support that, on the basis of what has been assessed, appropriate interventions to promote a better outcome will be effective through assertive outreach.

Past histories will contribute to what is being assessed in the present and if there are any inaccuracies, the evidence that supports what is believed to be the service perspective on the client's situation will outweigh their presentation. This circle of contagiousness further compounds the cycle of care access and delivery that permeates the reality of the Black individual's experience of psychiatric services.

It is within this climate that assertive outreach teams aim to develop a relationship with the individual. There is, however, a great deal of emphasis placed on the breakdown of the relationship with services and this is attributed to the client. This suggests that the problem is with the client and not with the services.

The measurement of the relationship is usually comprised with the taking of medication to sustain good mental health and removal of symptoms and behaviours associated with mental illness. The indicators being that the client has failed if they need to come back into hospital, usually against their will, and usually at a time when it is difficult to communicate any positive benefits in accepting this mode of assistance.

Concerns as to whether the client has the intention to comply are usually based on past histories or on the initial presentation. Any hesitations or misgivings based on an uncertainty as to whether an individual can be understood, trusted or even *believed*, will lead to a projection of the practitioner's attitudes and beliefs upon the client. For the Black individual, the concept of trustworthiness and being understood is historical and is rooted in racial stereotyping. Its presentation in assessment can and does have a detrimental and negative affect on the situation.

For the Black individual, this is further perpetuated with the notion that it is difficult to form relationships because of 'culture'. **Culture is signified as the reason for a perception of difficult communication. Culture is utilised to fulfil expectations as to how an individual is perceived and thus to promote a stereotypical view of an individual which will influence the assessment and the individual's presentation.** Above all, culture is often deployed as a reason to side-step the client's social needs (Fanon, 1959).

The fact that is not so easily considered is that in addition to the usual range of individual difference, there are further dimensions of difference, based upon tradition, ethnic diversity amongst Black people, class and gender, to mention just a few of the parameters that should be taken into consideration when Culture is presented as a singular objective on the basis of one's race.

What has been described is evident of a negative use of the framework that encapsulates how we as practitioners attempt to engage with clients who require some degree of support and assistance from psychiatric services.

This is not a good foundation on which to build a relationship of trust and respect. People are more likely not to value your opinion – or want to take up your suggestions as to how they can improve the quality of their life – if there is evidence of value and judgement statements that are influenced by racism, sexism, homophobia etc.

The inevitable outcome of non-compliance or disengagement at this point on the continuum is:

- a higher degree of hospital repeat admissions, usually enforced under the *Mental Health Act 1983*
- an increased use of medication as a means of treatment for what is then described as an enduring mental illness
- an increase in the diagnosis of schizophrenia/bi-polar disorders amongst this particular client group.

The above indicators are commonly presented as evidence of an inequality in the provision of mental health care through the psychiatric services. It is not just apparent in assertive outreach teams, but in the majority of services provided via the psychiatric agencies. Prior to the formation of these particular services, the issues that affected Black people were still evident in psychiatry. There has been extensive change in the way in which psychiatry is viewing people and how they hope to interact in a positive way to improve the individual's experience, but the statistics have not yet determined that these new innovations have improved the experience of Black people who have come into contact with it (Commander *et al*, 1997).

The Black and minority communities enter into the psychiatric arena with an awareness of this situation and consequently little trust or confidence in the hope of having a positive relationship with services that are set up in this way.

These inequalities in the delivery of good mental health care are evident on all pathways into mental health services that are predominantly accessed by African Caribbean clients and other minority groups.

The inequalities in assessment are evident at all stages on the pathways into psychiatric care. The presentation of someone's situation is evident at the GP's practice and in his or her initial assessment at Primary Care level. It is on this basis that they begin their journey through the system and the pathway that takes them to inpatient care, and intensive levels of support as previously described.

The pathway that leads to the 'listening therapies' and psychological intervention is much more difficult to access. This decision, again, is made on the basis of the initial and consequent assessments, which formulate a picture that the client is not suitable for counselling and therefore will not benefit from this alternative mode of treatment. It is less likely, therefore, that Black and minority clients will receive this form of treatment, which is further suggestion of inequalities in the receipt of appropriate mental health care and support.

This is applicable because of the inequality in how the host views others who are from other races. The evidence that Western psychiatry was developed within a racist and sexist framework is paramount in the work of Francis *et al*, (1989). They indicate the use of psychiatry as a means of control and a systematic cleansing of societies from undesirable elements or deviancies. In short, if not understood or recognised to be a threat, the problem was removed. The client therefore is the one with the problem and the need to conform to the host's framework of acceptability and values.

Alternatives in Assessment Through Community Outreach and Support

The delivery of good quality mental health care is based on formulating a relationship with the client that results in a more accurate assessment of what their needs are and their perspective on their presenting situation. This will result in a more effective care plan that will assist the practitioner to have a more positive and useful approach to the client's situation.

This way of working is integral to the Outreach and Community Support Team who have developed a way of working with individuals who require additional support from others, during critical points in their lives, which can affect their mental health.

The Team works in conjunction with all components of the Frantz Fanon Centre and other agencies in order to establish a more accurate assessment of the situation presented by the client.

The aim is to be responsive to the client's needs in contrast to the service's perception, which has a tendency to lead to conflict because of its focus on deviant behaviour and social control. We try to achieve a relationship with an individual through acknowledgement of the impact of racism and its effect on the individual's mental health and their basic survival in society. Awareness and knowledge of the pitfalls and danger zones on the typical pathways usually travelled by Black people in the psychiatric arena is paramount to understanding and assessing the realities in the presentation of a mental health problem. This should be evident as a means of providing preventative means of support to individuals at all levels of interaction with services.

On this basis, once Black and minority peoples come into contact with this form of Westernised psychiatry, their behaviour is viewed as abnormal (Fanon, 1967).

At the Frantz Fanon Centre, we offer an alternative mode of assessment, which aims to present a more accurate reflection of the client's perspective on their situation. The objective would be to enable the practitioner to have a more sensitive and appropriate relationship with the individual and their world, which would determine a more effective plan of care or interaction that enables the client to reach their potential and attain good mental health.

The framework of the assessment is based upon a humanistic approach, which aims to incorporate the reality of racism and how it impacts upon an individual's mental health. The basis of this approach emanates from the experience of the Black individual who has come into contact with psychiatry. However, we believe that this framework can be applied to other client groups in relation to whom similar attitudes, prejudices and value statements affect the social and clinical assessment of normality.

None of the stages works independently of each other. They can be recycled and work with each other, providing information for each stage reached.

Process of Working With Clients

Referral

The starting point of any process, including assessment, should begin with some analysis of what is presented from either the client or a representative, as a reason for requesting our involvement. Representation could be from the GP, other statutory agencies, non-statutory agencies or departments, clients' family, carer or friend. This is usually called a 'referral' and should comprise a statement of client need, awareness and consent for the service to become involved. It is part of the policy at the Frantz Fanon Centre that the client is aware of and consenting to the referral being made.

Self-referrals tend to be more accurate in the description of what is considered an informed choice, with an expectation of an effective outcome.

Very often, clients are referred to services of which they have no knowledge or understanding as to why this particular service can assist in meeting their needs or enabling some change in their situation. That the client is aware and is consenting to the referral indicates that some dialogue with the client as to their needs and choices has taken place.

Client consent encourages a mode that includes their own analysis as to their situation and indicates that the client is more likely to be prepared to look at entering into a relationship with the service.

Discussion of the referral with the team components then takes place in order to establish who are the most appropriate individual(s) to enter into the next phase of interaction with the individual. Experiences are taken into consideration when making this decision, as well as awareness and knowledge that may enhance a position of understanding of the situation. (It has been my experience that workers often describe their own needs or points of crisis as if they were the client's situation).

There is also a need to be aware of value statements and judgements made about individuals on the basis of their race/sexuality etc. It is necessary for us to be aware of racially stereotypical views and attitudes in the examination of the evidence that supports what is being described as individual symptomatology at this and subsequent stages of the assessment.

Pre-assessment Phase

The assessment process is divided into two main components: pre-assessment and assessment. The pre-assessment phase enables the practitioner to focus on developing an understanding of what the presenting realities are from the client's perspective and how this is impacting on the world around them.

Establishing a relationship with the client

It is at this point that interaction with the client is based on establishing a relationship. The relationship needs to be one that is built on trust, respect, confidentiality and mutual understanding. By doing so, it is more likely that the individual will open up to sharing their experiences with you, thus enabling the practitioner to have a more accurate picture of what the issues are.

Establishing a framework for assessment

The nature of the pre-assessment is to establish the framework for our enquiries and enable both client and practitioner to identify the type of evidence that is required for the full assessment. Concerns may include differences of opinion as to referral information and questions in relation to presenting diagnosis. Conflicting evidence is considered in relation to the client's experience and their understanding as to their unmet needs.

Consideration of 'risk'

If presented, the element of risk should be examined in context with a greater understanding of what defines the risk. Whilst operating within a framework of personal safety and safety to others, the practitioner needs to be observant of the wider parameters of risk, and potential risk, which include the client or individual as the victim, instead of the perpetrator.

Previous history

It is important to remember that presenting or past evidence will provide clues as to any misinformation or misleading representations of the client's situation. It is on the basis of some inaccurate/incomplete information and reporting that past histories are developed that have an impact on the client's presenting situation. It is important also to check for value statements/judgements based on racial identity and expectations of behaviour as symptomatic of cultural difference.

Descriptions of non-engagement can be presented as 'isolated, non-attendance of appointments, refusal to allow access.' This presentation of a resistance to having a relationship with the mental health agencies can be evident and prescriptive as a negative perception of the individual's ability to communicate and relate to the world around him.

This should promote further assessment into what the basis of past relationships has been and how they may have impacted upon the individual's desire to interact with others. It would be useful to avoid the pitfalls of previous attempts for meaningful engagement, by exploring what evidence there is to substantiate statements made.

Taking time for pre-assessment

It may take as many as three to five contacts with the individual to complete the basis of the framework and identify what components need to be involved, for further enquiry and investigation.

Assessment Phase

It is anticipated that as we enter into this point of the interaction with the individual, some basis of a relationship is already under way. There should be a transition of information that makes concrete the basis of the communication. It is here that you will be able to further check the evidence presented as 'objectives for the referral' in comparison to the client's needs and expectations.

There is a continuation in the process of collecting relative data that gives some meaning and understanding to the individual's situation. This may involve receiving further background information to the circumstances presented via family, friends and significant others, with the individual's permission. It is useful to consequently develop an awareness of any particular dynamics within the relationships of those involved with the individual.

It is imperative to note that it is the practitioner's analysis and interpretation of the presenting evidence that will have an impact on the client's situation and future relationship with the services. Recommendations made here will enable the client to commence on particular pathways into care.

Goals and objectives will have a greater chance of success, if the assessment of the situation or circumstances is accurate.

The prerequisites that were evident in the pre-assessment phase are to be continued in this stage of the assessment process. This will enable a continuation of the relationship-building that needs to be in evidence.

The holistic approach to assessment is paramount at this stage. By this we mean:

1 **Life events:** a full assessment of the client's personal circumstances, in terms of relationships and the influence of life events
2 **Sociological and economic factors:** a full presentation of sociological and economic factors that are impacting on the individual's wellbeing
3 **The impact of racism** in its introvert state (albeit that there is sufficient evidence to be aware of blatant, direct racism experienced by Black individuals in their pursuit of gaining access to what is provided by social and welfare systems); this also includes the aspect of a false perception of 'Black rage' and cultural imperatives
4 **Spiritual and emotional life:** consideration of all dimensions of a client's experience from an emotional and spiritual dimension, as well as from a psychological and physiological standpoint
5 **Physical factors:** exploration of whether there are any significant physical dysfunctions/deficiencies or dilemmas present that are impacting on the individual's mental health

1 Life events

One of the most common areas of concern in assessment is the concept of the individual and their relationships with family and close friends. Very often it is assumed that there is a disengagement from family and that the individual does not have any significant persons in their life. The assumptions are based on the perspective of 'the perfect family' from the practitioner.

Looking to the Future © Pavilion Publishing/Mental Health Foundation, 2000

By using the term 'significant other' it allows the client to express more freely who is currently in a significant relationship with them. This may not be a direct family member. By opening up the scope to explore what relationships the client is experiencing, we are assisted in identifying particular evidence to explore if there is any isolation, difficulties in forming relationships, or disengagement from the client's own community. These are common statements used to support evidence that contribute to the individual displaying behaviours described as symptomatic of psychosis or personality disorder.

This does not mean to say that the individual who has become separated from family friends and their community is, or is not, adversely affected in relation to their mental wellbeing. It seems more likely that the effects of isolation and displacement from one's community may have a more depressive outcome than that of a schizo-affective disorder (Fanon, 1959).

We must explore the ways in which life events are impacting on the client and whether there is any disparity in how they are coping on an emotional level.

2 Sociological and economic factors

Included in the assessment is an examination of social and economic situations that may be presented as problems experienced by the individual.

It is well documented that people from Black and minority communities experience racism and disadvantage in employment, housing, education and many other areas of life. These are all factors which are known to affect an individual's mental health in an adverse way. Therefore, the interpretation of the effect of any one of these sociological factors can result in misrepresentation of assessment outcomes based on analogies of race representation as a cultural 'norm', or as behaviours evident of symptoms of mental illness.

The colour of an individual's skin does not change the reality of poor housing and unemployment, but racism compounds the experience and adversely increases the potential for mental health crises. The assessment of how that is presented is paramount to what response or intervention is required.

3 The impact of racism

The impact of racism should be explored in relation to sociological factors to mental ill health, such as housing issues, finance, employment and education. This can also impact on children and family dynamics. The experience of Black people includes the constant oppression of institutional racism within their everyday lives: from school to social services, police, courts, prisons and psychiatric hospitals. This should be taken into consideration when making an assessment of basic need. There should be an acknowledgement of the role that could be played by advocacy and support to confront racist attitudes in relation to access to provision of welfare.

'Black rage'

As previously mentioned in this chapter, it is sometimes implied that the African Caribbean individual expresses emotion in a mode of catharsis with the implication that there is an exaggeration of grief and other emotions. The analysis of the presentation of 'Black rage' is an illustration of the perception of anger as a clinically abnormal and irrational behaviour. The concept of anger and Black people raises fear and anxiety and a need to control any situation that is thought to put society at risk (hooks, 1996). This can result in a contribution to a risk assessment which determines evidence that the client is 'dangerous, aggressive and at worse, is a risk to self or others.' These types of statements and labelling based on perceived cultural idiosyncrasies result in overuse of mental health legislation. The outcome is hospital admission by force. Compulsion makes it more difficult to form a relationship with the individual and predicts a more negative outcome and journey on a predicted pathway. This is the majority of Black people's experience within the psychiatric setting.

Culturally-defined behaviour

In the process of examination and assessment of the presentation of behaviours described as 'cultural' it is important to be aware of the pitfalls that can occur in practice. Behaviours that are not understood can be labelled as having a 'cultural' framework if the individual is not of the host culture and the behaviour has been seen before by other individuals from the same race.

These subtleties and variations of common translations of culture in relation to race are presented in the form of assessments that indicate that there are 'cultural issues' apparent. These are presented in assessment and can create obstacles and impediments to the client receiving an appropriate assessment. These also present as problems to the practitioner, thus labelling 'cultural diversity' as a negative factor in achieving appropriate levels of communication and relationships that contribute to a qualitative and accurate assessment of need. Culture is often spuriously cited as an obstacle to engagement when, in fact, the client's difference is actually being exaggerated.

The exaggeration of individual difference on the basis of culture leads to oversimplified generalisations to the whole group. In other words, the specific understanding of an individual situation is predetermined by cultural generalisations leading to the assumption that a practitioner or therapist from the same ethnic group is bound to be able to work with the client. The fact that the practitioner or therapist is from the same ethnic group of the client does not remove the obligation to have an understanding of the individual situation.

The utilisation of basic knowledge of one particular cultural ideology prevalent amongst those from the African Diaspora as a reference to explain the cultural characteristics of an individual, on the basis that they are of the same race can have a damaging effect on the relationship between the practitioner and the individual as it reconstructs and compounds institutional racism.

4 Spiritual and emotional life

In assessment it is important to have awareness and develop an understanding of the individual's spiritual beliefs and practices. This may present in ways that do not harmonise with the practitioner's spiritual framework and this can lead to a projection of our own values and beliefs on the individual's perception of what is conducive for their spiritual wellbeing. The importance of spirituality is especially crucial in the area of separating delusional and hallucinatory experience from religiosity.

When I talk of spirituality, I refer to the breath of life itself, the soul and spirit of the individual that incorporates their beliefs and framework of reference for living. This may or may not have some foundation in religious beliefs. The aim is to respect and value the individual's spirituality, acknowledge and understand its existence, without judgement and analysis in comparison to the practitioner's own criteria for spiritual wellbeing.

5 Physical factors

It is important also to recognise the possible influence of physical factors on a person's mental health. This includes, for example, awareness of any presenting disorders such as Sickle Cell Anaemia or Systemic Lupus Erythamatus. The psychological and emotional effect of these and other types of illnesses can have a severe impact on a person's mental health and there is a concern that symptoms presented can be attributed to severe mental illness, when in fact there is a physical cause.

Taking Time to Assess

The assessment, like the pre-assessment phase, may also take anything from between three and five contacts to complete, before sufficient information is collated to substantiate an accurate and effective evaluation of the individual's situation. This, coupled with a sensitive, workable relationship and an understanding of the external pressures that have contributed to the individual's presentation to services, should equip the practitioner with the confidence to plan workable aims and objectives that would constitute an effective plan of intervention suited to the individual's needs.

The Importance of Accuracy

An accurate assessment of physical, psychological and emotional behaviours and responses presented here would influence a change in the plan of care. This could be the provision of education and adequate support instead of hospitalisation and treatment for schizophrenia.

It is a crucial element of the assessment to ensure accuracy in relation to the interpretation of what is presented. Inaccuracies presented due to inequality in the mode of assessment can result in denying access to psychological interventions such as counselling and psychotherapy. The perception of the practitioner can be altered depending on how the client's experience is described and analysed through the language of the individual. The greater the degree of misunderstanding, the more likely that what is being heard becomes evident of a psychosis which is traditionally seen as less likely to be amicable to a psychotherapeutic mode of intervention. This also contributes to a consequent denial of the presence of depression as an outcome of experiences and even further dismisses evidence that indicates an individual's insight into their situation.

Conclusion

Although this process of assessment may take a relatively long period of time, the likelihood is that the outcome will be more accurate and more likely to produce a more productive relationship with the individual who needs to access support from mental health services.

The evidence that will support the practitioner's viewpoint as to the accuracy of the assessment will be if the outcome enables the client's problems and strengths to be clearly identified. The formation of goals and objectives that match the client's expectations of care will further prove the authenticity and accuracy of any assessment made.

Throughout the process there should be an opportunity for the individual to respond to their understanding of the process and how it is received. The need to constantly re-evaluate and assess what is being presented to the practitioner is an indicator of the complexities of human beings and how we relate and interact with the world around us. Awareness of what is a reality on the outside is a reflection of what is being internalised. The reality of the effect of racism and its effect on an individual's mental health is paramount when assessing the oppressive features that can consequence in mental ill health.

The eventual hope is that this mode of assessment will enable a reduction in the disproportionate amount of misdiagnosis in Black people and will also increase the access to more appropriate pathways of care.

Acknowledgement

I would like to thank Erroll Francis, Programme Director at the Frantz Fanon Centre for his ongoing encouragement and support, particularly whilst writing this chapter.

Bibliography

Browne, D., Francis, E. & Crowe, I. (1993) Black People, Mental Health and the Criminal Justice System. In: E. Francis, W. Watson & A. Grounds (Eds) *The Mentally Disordered Offender in the Era of Community Care - New Directions in Provision.* Cambridge: Cambridge University Press.

Commander, M.J., Cochrane, R., Sashidharan, S., Akilu, F. & Wildsmith, E. (1997) *Ethnicity and Mental Health Service Provision.* Birmingham: University of Birmingham.

Fanon, F. (1959) *Studies in a Dying Colonialism.* London: Earthscan Publications Ltd.

Fanon, F. (1967) *Black Skin, White Masks.* New York: Grove Press.

Francis, E., David, J., Johnson, N. & Sashidharan, S. (1989) Black People and Psychiatry in the UK: An Alternative to Institutional Care. *Psychiatric Bulletin* **13** 482–485.

hooks, b. (1996) *killing rage ending racism.* London: Penguin.

See also:

Mercer, K. (1986) Racism and Transcultural Psychiatry in the Power of Psychiatry. In: P. Miller & N. Rose (Eds) *Anti-racist Practice in Mental Health Assessment.* Cambridge: Polity Press.

Treatment? 1 *Mike Smith*

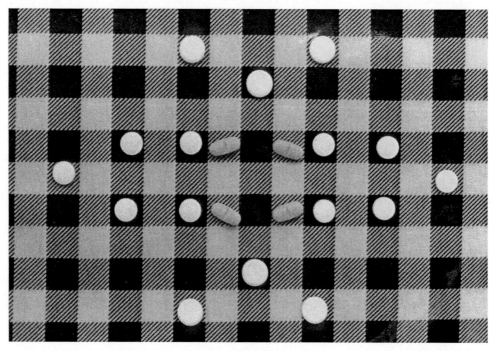

Treatment? 2 *Mike Smith*

Looking to the Future © Pavilion Publishing/Mental Health Foundation, 2000

Chapter 9

Building quality mental health services

Dawn Wakeling

Quality has become a buzzword in all health and social care services and throughout other public services such as education. Where we used to talk of *standards* – and even then not very often – *quality* now seems to be appearing everywhere, spearheaded by a number of government initiatives to drive up the quality of care and reduce variations in consumer experience. In mental health, the *National Service Framework For Mental Health* (DoH, 1998) and the White Paper, *Modernising Mental Health Services* (DoH, 1998) will have a huge impact on services. But this is not the end of it. There is a lengthy list of current initiatives and policies that all share the aim of regulating and improving the quality of UK health and social care.

This chapter outlines the growth of quality assurance in health care and the main policy drivers behind this. It explains what Quality Assurance (QA) is, and the benefits it can bring to service providers and users. It also considers how QA can be a tool for change in services: how we can use QA to support staff in their day-to-day work and to provide a better response to users' needs.

The Policy Context

The White Paper on NHS quality, *A First Class Service* (HSC1998/113) (DoH, 1998) introduced clinical governance, making all NHS organisations accountable for safeguarding high standards. In the White Paper, the then Health Secretary - Frank Dobson, emphasised the Government's determination 'to place quality at the heart of health care'. **Clinical governance** can be defined as being the framework that NHS organisations must use for ensuring quality. What this essentially does is require NHS organisations to have a coherent, organisation-wide strategy and system for QA, and ensure there is top level accountability for it. This, for many organisations, will involve combining things they do already, such as clinical audit, as part of a wider process. There is a new statutory duty for quality on NHS trusts and Primary Care Trusts to support its implementation.

Key components of clinical governance

- comprehensive and structured programme of quality improvement activity and monitoring
- clear policies for risk and professional performance management
- clear accountability for quality

Clinical governance strategies will be supported by an increased emphasis on lifelong learning for professionals, ensuring their skills and knowledge are up-to-date, safe and effective; and strengthening systems of professional self-regulation. These new initiatives clearly reflect the Government's response to public concern about the quality of treatment and care delivered by individual health care professionals, and the attention that these cases have received in the media. As well as increasing the individual professional's responsibility for their own performance and the duties of the professional body, clinical governance is an attempt to bring under corporate control the practice of individual practitioners.

Clinical governance is just one part of the Government's health care quality-strategy. Nationally, standards for services and guidelines on effective treatments and their use will be given via national service frameworks and the National Institute for Clinical Excellence (NICE). National Service Frameworks (NSF) will be produced for all health care specialities. They will set standards for services, define preferred service models and require local agencies to develop and implement plans for achieving NSF standards. A National Implementation Group will monitor the implementation of the National Service Framework and performance targets will be linked to wider NHS performance indicators.

The *National Service Framework For Mental Health* was issued in Autumn 1999. It set seven standards in five areas of mental health. These areas were defined as:

1   mental health promotion
2   primary care and access to services (two standards)
3   effective services for people with severe mental illness (two standards)
4   caring about carers
5   preventing suicide.

NICE will issue national guidelines on the effectiveness of health treatments, including non-drug treatment. It will appraise all new medications and is set to look at drugs used in the treatment of schizophrenia. NICE is intended to promote equity in access to treatment; by providing definitive guidance on treatments, it should ensure that situations that have occurred in the past – where treatments were not available in all health authority areas ('postcode prescribing') – no longer occur.

There is a stronger emphasis on performance measurement and monitoring in health services overall. The performance of health and social services will be measured in a different way via new national performance frameworks, and a national survey of patient and user experience. Services on the ground will be monitored by the Commission for Health Improvement (CHI), another new national body that will conduct reviews of all health services and in particular consider progress against national service framework standards.

Significant changes are also happening in the field of social care in mental health. The Government has announced the establishment of a parallel National Institute for Excellence in Social Care, and a Green Paper on quality in social care.

Best Value changes the basis for local authority purchasing of social care services, and replaces compulsory competitive tendering, where cost was the primary factor in decision-making. **Best Value charges local authorities to consider effectiveness and performance as the basis for purchasing decisions, via what are known as The Four Cs: Challenge, Consult, Compare, Compete.** Best Value will affect all those who provide social care services funded by local authorities. It also places responsibility on local authorities to involve their communities in purchasing strategies through consultation.

Other key developments in social care quality are that social care staff, such as social workers and care workers, will be regulated, with the introduction of the General Social Care Council in England and a Care Council for Wales. Day services will be accredited and a new National Care Standards Commission will replace local authority inspection units. It will register and inspect care homes, domiciliary care agencies and independent hospitals and clinics.

Addressing quality assurance in mental health and social care services appears inescapable, especially as it is not just coming from government. Umbrella bodies like the National Housing Federation have published quality frameworks for supported housing and risk management; many voluntary sector providers have produced their own service standards. The National Council of Voluntary Organisations currently runs a project devoted to encouraging charities of all types to implement quality assurance.

Using Quality

It is difficult not to relate these developments to public concern over a number of high profile incidents where the clinical skills or professional conduct of health and social care staff have come under scrutiny. Some of the efforts to increase equity could also be seen as part of a drive to reduce medication costs in the NHS. However, the Government's focus on the quality of health and social care services is in keeping with their approach to other public services and if we have to use Quality, it is important to see the positive forces behind it. Improved accountability in public services can only be a good thing. QA offers opportunities for services to be clearer about their purpose, and ensure they are offering the best possible response they can to service users. It also offers opportunities for meaningful user and whole-staff involvement in service development. The lessons from industry bear witness to this.

The Roots of Quality

Quality Assurance began in industry – to ensure safe and efficient construction – and subsequently gained popularity in the business world. The first quality 'management gurus' were from statistical and engineering backgrounds and applied these techniques to wider business practice. Quality Control took off because companies were able to show cost savings and improved performance and customer satisfaction. People at the forefront of promoting quality assurance were management thinkers such as Deming, whose ideas were widely used in Japan where Quality Assurance techniques have been credited with major responsibility for their post-war economic success.

Although used in the private sector for many years, Quality Assurance did not become popular in the health service until the 1970s and '80s, when approaches such as Total Quality Management began to be used.

There are some key lessons that mental health services can take from the business experience of Quality Assurance:

1   The first is that QA needs to *consider improvements* as opposed to only *correcting defects*. Without this, the same mistakes will be repeated. Current Quality Assurance systems tend to focus on continuous evaluation and improvement as a result

2   The second concerns our approach to QA. Often, when faced with the requirement to implement a QA system, staff are put off by the effort and resources required to implement it – whereas in fact they should think of the cost of *not* doing it right first time. Organisations of all kinds incur huge costs in terms of time and resources by not doing it right first time, and in health and social care there is also a potential human cost to service users

3   The third lesson to take from the business experience of QA is that where quality techniques have really made a difference, frontline staff have been key players. This is not to deny the responsibility of management to implement QA but to recognise the value of a bottom-up approach, which uses the unique knowledge of frontline staff and builds on their commitment

Perhaps most importantly, business thinkers can give us ways to define and work with the notion of quality. As Peter Senge wrote: 'By "quality", we mean all the things that matter to a customer'. All you need to do is change the word 'customer' to 'service user'.

What is Quality Assurance?

Quality Assurance measures organisations: their systems, activities, and outcomes. It gives you a snapshot of the organisation. This can help you to achieve greater clarity of purpose, knowledge of your effectiveness and the benefits you offer to service users. At the very least, it should demonstrate that the service is doing what it is meant to do! One of the basic tenets of ISO 9000 – one of the longest-established quality systems – is: *Say what you do...and then do what you say.* This may seem so obvious as to be redundant but it is important to remember that even today many providers are not able to show how their activities match their mission statement, or state precisely the benefits and outcomes of the services they do offer.

By a **Quality Assurance System**, we mean the framework used for defining quality, the standards we aim to achieve, and the methods we use to measure our progress.

The **Framework** is simply the format used to divide the organisation or services you are measuring into manageable chunks, based on the beliefs held about what constitutes good quality. So, the ISO system makes an organisation capture, via a set of written procedures, how it wants to work, in order to monitor and correct any failure to meet them and implement longer-term improvements so it does not happen again. The Excellence Model uses nine headings to encompass all organisational activities, from leadership of the organisation through to staffing issues, and measuring customer satisfaction and performance results.

Standards are written statements of what your service or organisation aims to achieve. They should clearly state what people can expect from the service. There can be a difference in what standards are intended to achieve, however. Some standards may set a minimum or baseline achievement, whereas others in a system appear to be aspirational.

If we use an example from the *National Service Framework for Mental Health*, we can see this difference. Standard Four states that:

> *'all mental health service users on CPA should...have a written copy of their care plan which includes the action to be taken in a crisis by the service user, their carer, and their care co-ordinator, advises their GP how they should respond if the service user needs additional help, (and) is regularly reviewed by their care co-ordinator.'*

This is a baseline standard that services should be able to demonstrate clearly that they meet.

Standard One in the Framework (see below) however is an aspirational standard. Demonstrating that your service met this standard would be more complex, as it refers to factors that are difficult to measure such as health improvements and reduction of discrimination in the wider population, and where there is no obvious end point. Agencies would be able to identify specific activities that contributed to meeting it, however, such as running educational programmes on mental health in schools and assessing the improvement of knowledge about mental health in participants.

National Service Framework for Mental Health

Standard One:

> *'To ensure health and social services promote mental health and reduce the discrimination and social exclusion associated with mental health problems, health and social services should:*
>
> * *promote mental health for all, working with individuals and communities*
>
> * *combat discrimination against individuals and groups with mental health problems, and promote their social inclusion.'*

There are a wide variety of methods used in assessing how well a service measures up to its quality standards. Two key differences are between **self-assessment** and **accreditation** systems.

Accreditation is where an external agency assesses whether you have met the standards and usually involves giving an award. Awards usually have a limited life-span. The Chartermark, Investors in People and the ISO 9000 awards are all examples of accredited awards.

Self-assessment systems usually do not involve an external award but rely on the service assessing its own performance only, usually on a repeated basis. The rationale behind self-assessment is that getting a 'badge' for your quality can have the effect of organisations thinking they can immediately stop addressing quality.

The Excellence Model is a self-assessment system (although confusingly there are some awards companies can enter but they are not the main aim of the system). Self-assessment involves a range of activities and should not be primarily a paper exercise: stakeholder workshops and conferences, teams assessing each other against the standards, customer/user and staff-satisfaction surveys should all be used. These can give an opportunity for real debate about the service and can lead to change that involves all the service's stakeholders in a positive way. Even if your service is aiming for an accredited award, methods for stakeholder involvement in quality assurance and a rolling programme for assessment and improvement should be used.

Quality assurance systems can be **generic** – ie about being a well-run organisation in general – or they can be **specific** – ie about a particular service area such as mental health.

Investors in People, the ISO series and the Excellence Model are all generic quality systems that are used in the private, public and voluntary sectors by very different organisations. Specific systems for mental health include Quartz, the Health Advisory Service 2000 Standards and Health Quality Service accreditation.

The voluntary sector has developed quality systems specifically for charities: PQASSO is a system for the smaller charity, while Quality First is a system for entirely volunteer-run groups. Many individual providers have also developed their own specific standards for their services.

Quality Assurance offers a key to organisational learning and development. By assessing and reviewing services, providers can get a baseline measurement on which new goals can be based. This is often referred to as *continuous improvement*, which refers to a cycle of quality assurance activities to assess the service, plan improvements, implement them, and review the difference they have made, before beginning the cycle again.

Learning about the organisation or service via Quality Assurance allows providers to compare performance with similar organisations or services. This is called *benchmarking*, and is not about beating others or establishing league tables, but about *learning* from others. Many companies have significantly improved their efficiency and outcomes through benchmarking, although not always through looking for obvious comparisons. A lipstick maker and a bullet manufacturer famously compared production processes with very good results!

What It Can Give You: A Quality Future

Many providers have implemented QA in response to purchaser requirements but this should never be the main reason for doing it. Quality Assurance offers opportunities to galvanise a whole organisation. It systematically recognises existing achievements – it proves what you do well, as well as showing you what could be improved. By giving you accurate information, it supports better planning and management.

The existence of written standards makes explicit your commitment to service users and what users, purchasers and the public can expect of you. It improves accountability to the same groups by demonstrating your achievements, how the service is addressing weaknesses and a commitment to do this continuously. This leaves the service in a stronger position when dealing with difficulties such as threats to funding or public concern about community-based services.

For mental health services, quality assurance can be used to improve two important areas: service-user involvement and the implementation of service philosophy and values. The standards followed and the methods used to assess against them can both provide opportunities to actively engage with service users; support the development of services that are shaped by users at all levels, in management, planning and delivery; and provide improved responses to individual needs.

Developing or implementing a quality system can give providers and the whole staff team a focus for defining and agreeing their service philosophy and values. More importantly, QA can be used to assess how values – such as those expressed in mission statements and equal opportunities policies – are put into action on a day-to-day basis.

For QA to deliver what it promises, mental health service-providers need, in the words of an Irish company who used QA, 'to take it, shape it and use it'. Behind what can seem like a bewildering array of technical terms are practical ways of starting dialogue in services, getting involvement and commitment from people and creating imaginative solutions to real organisational needs. In the private sector it has been a way of leading major change, often from the bottom up. For it to be successfully used however, we need to ensure that we train and support staff in using QA, and enable the equal participation of service users in QA activities.

In mental health services we need to be sure that the QA activity we use enhances our service philosophy and values and practitioners' interpretation of them. We need to move away from viewing QA as an add-on activity to our core work and instead find ways of integrating it in our daily routines: for, how can quality not be at the heart of what we do in mental health care services?

References

Astbury R., & Mayall, H. (1997) *A Map of Quality Standards: A Guide to understanding quality systems in the voluntary sector.* London: NCVO.

Crosby, P. (1979) *Quality is Free.* Victoria, Australia: Signet Books.

Department of Environment, Transport and Regions (1998) *Modern Local Government: In Touch With the People.* White Paper. London: DETR.

Department of Environment, Transport and Regions (1998) *Achieving Best Value Through Quality Management.* Discussion paper. London: DETR.

Department of Health (1998) *A First Class Service.* HSC 1998/113. London: Department of Health.

Department of Health (1998) *A First Class Service - Quality in the NHS.* Consultation document. London: DoH.

Department of Health (1999) *A First Class Service - Feedback on consultations.* HSC 1999/033. London: DoH.

Department of Health (1999) *A New Approach to Social Services Performance.* Consultation Document. London: DoH.

Department of Health (1999) *National Service Framework for Mental Health: Modern Standards and Service Models.* London: DoH.

Department of Health (1998) *National Service Frameworks* HSC 1998/074. London: DoH.

Department of Health (1998) *Modernising Health and Social Services - National Priorities Guidance 1999/00 2001-02.* London: DoH.

Department of Health (1998) *Modernising Mental Health Services - Safe, Sound & Supportive.* White Paper. London: DoH.

Department of Health (1998) *Modernising Social Services: Promoting Independence, Improving Protection, Raising Standards.* CM4169 White Paper. London: DoH.

Department of Health (1997) *The New NHS: Modern, Dependable.* CM 3807 White Paper. London: DoH.

European Foundation for Quality Management and The British Quality Foundation (1999) *The EFQM Excellence Model 1999: Public and Voluntary Sector.* Belgium: EFQM.

Investors in People UK (1998) *How to Become an Investor in People.* London: IIP.

Investors in People UK (1998) *The Investors in People National Standard.* London: IIP.

Leiper, R., Pilling, S. & Lavender, T. (1992) *The Quartz Manual: Implementing a Quality Review System.* Brighton: Pavilion Publishing.

Local Government (Best Value and Capping) Bill (Dec 1998).

Local Voices: Modernising Local Government in Wales (1998) White Paper. Welsh Office.

NCVO (1998) *Quality in the Voluntary Sector.* Quality Standards Task Group, NCVO.

NHS Executive (1998) *The New NHS - A National Framework for Assessing Performance.* London: Department of Health.

Onyett, S. (1999) *The National Service Framework: a commentary and summary.* Unpublished.

ISO (1994) *Quality Systems: Model for quality assurance in design, development, production, installation and servicing.* ISO 9001.

Senge, P. (1993) *The Fifth Discipline: The Art and Practice of Becoming a Learning Organisation.* Century/Arrow.

Social Services - Building for the Future (March 1999), White Paper. Welsh Office.

That Place on the Hill

When I was young
We would often ride on a bus
Past that place on the hill;
There were pigs and horses
On the side visible to the public
The funny farm they called it.

We would make jokes about the place
And stare at the people
When they ventured out into the street
But fear made us keep our distance.

I would join in the jokes
Even though
I was a fucked-up schoolboy
Who was sometimes considered backward
Other times told to pull his socks up,
Like everyone else
I needed my scapegoats.

Unaware
I didn't realise
Who had heard of ECT and Major Tranquillisers?
It's the way they are
I thought
So different from us
The crazy ones.

Some years later
In my mid-twenties
I got free board and lodging
In that place on the hill,

The world outside became a frightening place
Many hostile voices
Many impossible situations.

The animals have gone
But the buses still went past
The funny farm
Became a Mental Hospital
Became a Psychiatric Hospital
Became a Psychiatric Institution.

I found out about Major Tranquillisers and ECT,
Scheming psychiatrists
The authority figures
We are taught to look up to
Now they become symbols of fear.

The Psychiatric Institution became a prison
When there seemed no way out
No hopeful tomorrow
The world outside mocked and discriminated.

Praying for strength,
Someone to trust,
A helping hand,
A friendly face,
It becomes easy for any of us
To want to seek refuge
In that place on the hill.

I struggled on
A little damaged
I found wisdom
A sense of awareness
That I can sometimes communicate
I value what I have learnt from surviving.

Frank Bangay, February 1995

Arrive in Time *Jeremy Wooldridge*

Today
I went uphill
My confinement is real
Tomorrow will never arrive
In time

Looking to the Future © Pavilion Publishing/Mental Health Foundation, 2000

Ways of Working

Sleepless Nights 1 *Chrissy S.*

Sleepless Nights 2 *Chrissy S.*

Looking to the Future © Pavilion Publishing/Mental Health Foundation, 2000

Chapter 10

Community support workers

Alison Murray

In the UK, community support workers (also known as community care workers or community aides) are people who do not hold professional mental health qualifications and who work with people with a diagnosis of mental illness in an 'enabling' role. They provide direct care and support in the service user's own home and community. They generally work either:

- as part of a local Community Mental Health Team (CMHT)
- in a team linked to it
- in another mental health provision; or
- attached to a primary care team.

They may be employed by either health/social services, a voluntary or private organisation.

Brief History of the Role of Community Support Workers

In the past, more people with a mental illness diagnosis were in hospital for longer periods of time, often many years. When discharged they were in the care mainly of their GP and community psychiatric nurses. Nowadays, with improvements in the knowledge and treatment of mental illness, people can be helped to remain well living at home; hospital stays are much shorter. In addition to this, many of those who have spent many years in hospital are now able to be cared for in the community. The Care Programme Approach (Department of Health, 1990) heralded the start of developing local services to care for the mentally ill.

So what are the factors which help to keep people well? As well as mental health treatments such as drug therapy, psychotherapy and counselling, other factors which help people stay out of hospital include:

- stable housing
- sufficient money
- the ability to care for oneself – to shop, cook, clean etc
- the ability to manage the pressures which mental illness imposes.

Mental illness can often mean people find it hard to get back to work or education; even trying to join in local community activities can become very difficult and the community itself is not always understanding. Having a supportive network of friends and family is helpful but often, particularly for people with severe and enduring mental illness, these social and emotional supports are limited or absent. Also, with the increasing mobility of the population, people can be separated from their families. People with severe and enduring mental illness are often eventually drawn into the larger conurbations and drift into the inner city. All these factors may contribute to someone becoming very isolated and alone.

Keeping people well in the community means that the multidisciplinary Community Mental Health Team (CMHT) and the support services have a very important role. The professionally-trained members of the CMHT have, of course, many demands on their time and expertise and many of these factors in keeping people well do not specifically need their input. This is where community support workers have a strong and important role to fulfil. Indeed, as they are often local people, they excel in this role, knowing the community, the resources and the opportunities often better than the 'imported' mental health professionals. Trained, supported and supervised, they can fulfil many of these important activities.

It is likely that the different employers of support workers stem from the fact that health and social care services overlap and it remains unclear which agency has the responsibility for provision. Historically, local authority staff have been working with a variety of client groups for many years though not until comparatively recently with the mentally ill. There was, therefore, a good solid structure of organisation on which local authorities could build to develop teams of support workers. Health Trusts recognised the valuable service that support workers could provide and began, in the early 1990s, to create posts in CMHTs and nowadays most, if not all, teams employ such workers. A smaller number of support-worker posts have been created in (and work flexibly around) specialist housing for the mentally ill and in day centres and primary care teams.

Support Workers and their Current Role

Who are support workers?

A major study on support workers and their work in eight areas in England (Murray *et al*, 1997) found that support workers were generally well educated (around 20% were graduates) and were from a wide variety of occupational backgrounds. More women than men were employed and the men tended to be slightly older and re-entering the job market as a second career or after redundancy. The average support worker was in their thirties but there was a wide age range from around 20 to 60 years.

As well as the diversity in their previous occupations – farmer, clerk, spray painter, restaurateur (few had previous health or social care experience) – and the subsequent variety of skills these people were bringing to their work, the researchers found these were people with many active personal interests such as sport, yoga, dressmaking, painting and decorating, creative writing; they even found an animal beautician(!).

These findings about the varied skills and abilities of support staff echo a previous finding in the United States about the diversity of community support staff (Williams *et al,* 1994). They point out the value of differing interpersonal styles, people who are energetic and have a sense of 'can do' in working with the very different needs of individual service users. A recent UK study of users' views (Meek, 1998) evaluating the role of health care assistants in a community health-intensive support team, found that users greatly valued their client-centred approach and personal qualities.

From anecdotal evidence, it seems there are comparatively few mental health service users who work as community support workers in the UK. However, the numbers are slowly increasing. Of course, they have a unique insight into the difficulties faced and with proper support can become effective members of the team. In the USA 'mental health consumers' (users) have been employed as case-management aides; in other countries, for example Australia, support workers are involved in work with the indigenous populations and ethnic minorities.

With which client groups do they work?

In the UK, support workers may work with several different client groups:

- older adults with a mental illness diagnosis
- adults with severe mental illness such as schizophrenia

- mothers with post-natal depression
- people with anxiety disorders

and others.

Those workers linked with primary care teams may act as 'befrienders' or linkworkers and combine elements of mental health care, general health care, advocacy, and gender and race support-links between the service user, their family and the primary care team.

What is their role?

Support workers follow a care plan devised by the mental health team working with a service user, and they work on a regular basis helping people with mainly practical tasks in maintaining a home, self care, helping, making or sustaining friendships and so on. They also introduce the user to the wider community facilities. Most importantly they offer emotional support, and some are trained to monitor the taking, and side effects, of medication, or to follow a programme designed by a mental health professional to help a user gain confidence in a difficult area in their lives. They are not *themselves* mental health professionals and the boundary of their role is clear.

Increasingly, experienced support workers are asked to take on the 'keyworker' role for some users which requires that they co-ordinate and liaise with other staff providing care for their client, writing reports and attending various important meetings regarding their care. These responsibilities are often given to the support worker as, of all members of the team, they have the greatest knowledge and rapport with the user and the most regular contact. Advocacy is seen as another role for the support worker, although this is now developing as a discrete service.

How are they trained?

Most support workers undertake initially an induction programme which typically includes:

- orientation to local services
- the role of the support worker
- how the support role fits into the local services
- an introduction to mental illness
- the needs of people with mental illness
- boundaries of the support worker role
- Health and Safety
- record keeping
- the importance of communication
- the role of the day-to-day supervisor(s)
- arrangements for support.

In services adjacent to university towns, some university departments run dedicated vocational courses for support workers but generally, most support workers are encouraged to obtain NVQ validations at either level 2 or 3. In-house courses – usually run by the local authority social services, NHS Trusts or local mental health voluntary agencies – are generally provided on an ongoing basis, often as part of multidisciplinary team training.

Detailed training programmes for people working with the mentally ill have been more fully described from services in the USA rather than those in the UK (Gibeau, 1993; Simon *et al*, 1993; Brook *et al*, 1989).

Now that the potential of support workers has become clearer, consideration needs to be given to a range of training opportunities that should be available at both basic and advanced levels and relate directly to quality in service provision. The Certificate in Community Mental Health Care, launched by the Mental Health Foundation in 2000, is an example of this.

How the Role Fits into the Local Mental Health Service

This depends very much on the local configuration of health and social care services in each district. The key issue is how the providers of support worker services relate to those responsible for the mental health care of the individual. The problems of poor communication between different agencies or providers of care are well known and regrettably this has very occasionally led to disastrous consequences. It cannot be over-emphasised that the links between social care and health must be clear and regular both from those staff 'on the ground' and their managers. This is easiest where support workers are employed by the NHS Trust as they are in constant touch with their professional colleagues. Other providers need to ensure those links are in place and maintained. This is critical to the quality of the care plan delivered by the support worker, making it both meaningful and relevant, and also to the health of the service user and the safety of all.

The Evidence for Their Effectiveness

A US study (Godley *et al*, 1988) was one of the first studies reporting on the work of non-professionally trained people with the mentally ill. They describe the additional beneficial outcomes for users who had support workers finding that users had more new activities, better housing, did more shopping, learnt to keep medicine charts and that their physical activity increased, with associated weight loss. Since then there has been growing evidence internationally about the efficacy of such staff (Kleiner & Drews, 1992; Williams *et al*, 1994). In the UK, Murray and her colleagues (Murray *et al*, 1997) found specifically that support workers in CMHTs and social services teams:

- were valued by their colleagues and managers as practical workers with a good sense of the boundaries of their work
- had increased the quality of users' lives and built a key relationship with them

- undertook a wide range of duties covering practical tasks (money management, shopping, leisure activities, finding flats etc), giving social and emotional support (helping users communicate with their families, establishing and sustaining social networks) and mental and physical health care (eg assisting in maintaining a healthy lifestyle, monitoring medication compliance, monitoring risks, communicating with the GP over physical health concerns)
- appeared to influence the nature of work of their professional colleagues, especially mental health nurses if in CMHTs
- freed up professionals' time.

In a random sample of service users in the same study (where n= 44)

- 100% would recommend support workers to other users
- users rated support workers highly on aspects of the 'working alliance' (the therapeutic relationship formed with a client) for availability, trustworthiness and good understanding of their problems
- users reported that they found them non-threatening and supportive without a professional 'label' attached to them
- users confirmed that the types of tasks support workers helped them with were those which they themselves rated as most important and found most helpful.

Thus, to date, support workers appear to be contributing positively to services. Of course, they do have some advantages over their professional colleagues in that they generally have lower caseloads and are able to spend more time working with users directly. The quality and continuity of these relationships are keys to good outcomes for people with severe mental illness (Solomon & Draine, 1994; Frank & Gunderson, 1990).

There has been some recent evidence about the effectiveness of volunteer support workers working with women with depression in inner cities. The 'freshstart' experiences which support workers were able to provide, together with the absence of new severe stressors and a standard attachment style were found to be good predictors of remission (Harris *et al,* 1999).

Growing awareness of the particular needs from minority ethnic communities has resulted in link-worker schemes attached to primary care teams. The value of these schemes is reviewed by Gillam and Levenson (1999) from the King's Fund who consider them an important resource, too often untapped.

For users who are employed as support workers there is positive evidence of their ability to sustain the work from a US study, with managers rating them 'very highly'. A two year follow-up study found that there had been only brief periods of ill health and over half of the original workers were still employed (Sherman & Porter, 1991).

Issues Concerning Management and Support

At the heart of any good community mental health service are:

- good organisation and management
- adequate resources
- appropriate and adequate training for staff
- appropriately-sized case loads
- good team liaison
- care planning with clear and explicit aims and support for staff.

This is the framework within which support workers can best operate. Creating a service and managing support workers within that service requires planning and a culture of sharing skills and teamworking which recognises the value of input from support workers.

Supervision reporting-lines need to be clear and active. The supervisor is usually a social worker, occupational therapist or community mental health nurse. It is important that, no matter what the supervisor's specific professional background, they work 'in the field' and are fully aware of the needs of individual users and their problems. These professionally qualified staff have to adjust to monitoring, perhaps for the first time, staff who do not 'fit' into the known hierarchy of staff. The Nursing Research Units' (University of London) report (1997) recommended that *'nurses must have sound clinical knowledge to monitor support workers and learn to delegate while retaining accountability and control'*, and that *'support workers should have **full member** status within the team'*.

Supervision and support for support workers should be provided on a regular basis. Murray *et al* (op. cit) found that support workers received supervision more frequently than other staff (usually fortnightly) and that both managers and support workers themselves felt this was essential. The work is often taxing and support workers need to be continuously inventive and persistent to improve the quality of the lives of the users with whom they work. They therefore require support and understanding themselves and continuous on-the-job training to maintain this approach and increase their skills.

Recent approaches to care require a *team approach* to include team leaders, professionals, support workers and service users. After a period of time for settling in, cohesion within teams is bringing about new ways of working. Corrigan and McCracken (1999) highlight the need for this by advocating that psychosocial techniques be taught not as individual skills but as a team. For, without recognising the 'team context' users may suffer inconsistency of approach and staff may lose the valuable help of positive feedback and reciprocal support. As the workers with the most contact with service users, this approach would greatly assist support workers.

The Debate Over a New Profession?

There is a continuing debate about the role of support workers and whether they could or should be formalised into a 'profession'. Professional status brings very positive benefits – regulating approved workers and setting common standards of training which lead to better public understanding and expectations of the role. It also brings – importantly for the worker – status, all positive benefits.

There are however some problems. There is a lack of a *distinct* role for support workers. Their duties carry them across several existing professional boundaries. Also, they are not *autonomous* workers and are line-managed and supervised by professional staff.

Another issue is that the role often has local variability – for very sensible reasons – and it is the very flexibility of the role which often makes it so useful. The variability of the role may depend on the needs of the specific client group and the service. Also, the variability may be associated with the particular skills of the worker recruited, for example, for their expertise in benefits or housing issues.

It has been debated whether the regulatory authority of a profession would prevent abuse from direct care workers. Clearly this is a very important issue as users and their families must have confidence in staff, especially those who work with them in their own homes. Whether this requires a regulatory body is debatable. Good personnel practice at local level should ensure that only suitable people are recruited and continue to be employed. Proper personnel-recruitment procedures, employment checks and regular appraisals and supervision are critical.

Key Challenges for the 21st Century

Recognition

Many support workers have most job satisfaction from this aspect of their work and have no particular desire to train as a professional or aspire to management. In order to continue to motivate staff to remain in what is a rewarding though often demanding and frustrating post, services must find ways of showing how the role is valued. This is not necessarily through financial reward (though salaries must be realistic for the duties and responsibilities undertaken), but through their attitudes to the contribution of support workers. They may also be able to contribute constructively to service planning and development. Certainly their knowledge would be very helpful given how attuned they are to users' needs.

Teamworking

Treating support workers as equal partners in a team remains a challenge. The information which support workers bring back on a day-to-day basis is critical and keeps other team members fully in touch with the user and their needs. The language used may be 'non technical', and possibly more jargon-free, thus professionals may need to listen more carefully. Team leaders and team members must also adjust to monitoring and supervision and make opportunities for on-the-job training.

Research

We know the value of 'the working relationship' with service users. We now need to identify what the aspects or components of this relationship are. The results may aid us in developing practices and partnerships in services which aid and do not hinder the development of such key alliances.

Finally

It is not often that being described as 'ordinary' is seen as a compliment but this is how users of mental health services have often positively described community support workers. Doing 'ordinary' things and living a normal life is an aspiration which many people with mental illness have difficulty in achieving. Having someone willing to help on a regular basis when needed – to shop and cook a meal with you, or accompany you when you go out or play sport, or sort out worries about housing and benefits – is greatly welcomed. As support workers are also trained to understand some of the difficulties that mental illness imposes, and can provide rapid access to trained mental health professionals, this is a valuable bonus. Such is the impact that support workers have made in the relatively short time since such posts have been created.

Good news is sometimes elusive in mental health and it is encouraging that NHS Trusts and social services – often working in partnership with innovative voluntary agencies – have been able to develop imaginative support services that appear to give help exactly where users themselves see their priorities for care. A solid foundation is being laid for delivering effective help where users most value it. Future developments require similar careful planning and consolidation.

References

Brook, S., Fantanopoulos, I., Johnston, F. & Goering, P. (1989) Training Volunteers to Work With the Chronic Mentally Ill in the Community. *Hospital and Community Psychiatry* **40** (8) 853–855.

Corrigan, P. & McCracken, S. (1999) Training Teams to Deliver Better Psychiatric Programs. *Psychiatric Services* **50** (1) 43–45.

Department of Health (1990) *The Care Programme Approach for People With a Mental Illness.* DOH HC 23/LASS (90). London: DoH.

Frank, A. & Gunderson, J. (1990) The Role of the Therapeutic Alliance in the Treatment of Schizophrenia. *Archives of General Psychiatry* **47** 228–236.

Gibeau, J. (1993) Training Paraprofessionals for Psychiatric Support. *Caring* April 36–42.

Gillian, S., Levenson, R. (1999) Linkworkers in Primary Care (editorial). *British Medical Journal* **319** 6 November, 12–15.

Godley, S., Sabin, M., McClure, C., Smerton, M. & Manion, L. (1998) Paid Friends for Frequent Recidivists: an Evaluation of a Multi-facteted Community Aide Program. *Psychosocial Rehabilitation Journal* **11** (3) 29–39.

Harris, T., Brown, G., & Robinson, R. (1999) Befriending as an Intervention for Chronic Depressed Women in an Inner City. *British Journal of Psychiatry* **174** 225–232.

Kleiner, R. & Drews, D. (1992) Community-based Treatment of Psychiatric Disorders in the AS and Norway: Insights For New Service Delivery Systems. *International Journal of Social Psychiatry* **38** 95–106.

Murray, A., Shepherd, G., Onyett, S. & Muijen, M. (1997) *More Than a Friend: the Role of Community Support Workers.* London: The Sainsbury Centre for Mental Health.

Meek, I. (1998) Evaluation of the Role of the Health Care Assistant Within a Community Health Intensive Support Team. *Journal of Nursing Management* **6** 11–19.

Nursing Research Unit (1997) *The Changing Needs and Education of Mental Health and Learning Disability Nurses.* University of London: Department of Nursing Studies.

Sherman, P. & Porter, R. (1991) Mental Health Consumers as Case Management Aides. *Hospital and Community Psychiatry* **42** (5) 494–498.

Solomon, P. & Draine, J. (1994) Satisfaction With Mental Health Treatment in a Randomised Trial of Consumer Case Management. *Journal of Nervous and Mental Disease* **82** (3) 179–183.

Simon, P., Morse, E., Speier, T. & Ofosky, H. (1993) Training Older Adults to be Case Management Aides. *Hospital and Community Psychiatry* **44** (12) 1162–1165.

Williams, M., Forster, P., McCarthy, G. & Hargreaves, W. (1994) Managing Case Management: What Makes it Work? *Psychosocial Rehabilitation Journal* **18** (1) 49–60.

Food and Shelter

So strange it is this world today
The old people walk up and down with the shakes
It's part of their illness it is said
But there is a different explanation
They have been caught in an oppressive situation.

Dumped in Victorian Institutions so long ago
Through situations in living that we know and ignore,
But psychiatric drugs are no solution to human needs
They just leave people to pace corridors
Broken and defeated.

All we needed was food
All we needed was shelter
A roof above our heads in hostile weather
A sanctuary to go to when times got tough
No, not these dark institutions.
Tell me,
Do you know the true meaning
Of the word 'asylum?'

So strange it is
So strange,
So strange,
The story repeats itself day after day
In a society built at a competitive pace
That wants to hide those who become seen as a disgrace
Because they find a more sensitive way of living,
But that disgrace reveals itself
In rejection and loneliness.

So you hide from the neighbours
Your 'backward' son;
So you hide from the neighbours
Your 'sick' daughter
Or so you call her,
But what have they done wrong?
Tell me, tell me; can you answer?

Some of us hide in hostels and lodging rooms
Lonely rides on buses to the next possible opportunity
Some of us get controlled by long-term injections
A community nurse to call
With a needle at the ready,
But drugs that control are no solution
To heartbreak and loneliness.

All we needed was food
All we needed was shelter
A roof above our heads
To keep us dry and warm
A friendly arm around us
To comfort us
When times got tough
And we lived with impossibilities.

So why do you take me here, to these dark institutions?
Tell me, do we ever think about the true meaning
Of the word 'asylum'?

So strange it is the way we stigmatise,
So strange it is the way we categorise,
Keep away from those funny people
'They're different from us,' the crowd all say.
But did you ever look into my eyes
And see the fear I'm feeling?
Well what can you say?
That funny person might have been your friend
In a different time and place
It's just that situations make us change.

So strange it is,
So strange,
So strange,
We look for a fault inside the person
And ignore the situation.

But the ghetto just changes to suit the times
And the image of the mad person becomes so stereotyped
But it's much easier to control a rebel that way
As we do our funny little walks down endless mazes,
But how did we get to be here in the first place?

All we needed was food
All we needed was shelter
A roof above our heads in stormy weather
Someone who was understanding
We could have understood each other's needs.

So strange this world today
So strange indeed.

Frank Bangay, August 1985

Food and Shelter, written in the Summer of 1985, relates to some of
my personal experiences during the period of 1976–1978, and also
to experiences of other people whom I knew at the time. It is to do
with the revolving door system that we can get caught up in once
we enter the psychiatric system as a user/recipient of the services.
Too often decisions are made on our behalf and we can end up
going back and forth between hospital and hostel without there
seeming any way forward: what survivors used to refer to as the
web of psychiatry. When we are discharged from a psychiatric
hospital, we can often return to the situation which caused our
distress in the first place (whatever that distress may be). Where is
the road forward? It is true we get food and shelter in a psychiatric
institution, but we also get labels which can prove to be very
disempowering and single us out of society.

The original meaning of the word 'asylum' was a place of safety,
place of sanctuary. This can be at odds with some of our real
experiences of the psychiatric system.

July 1997

From the series "Millview Hospital" Millview Garden: Hope for the Future *Olive M.*

Holding On To Peace and Tranquility, An Escape *Leila Atherton*

Looking to the Future © Pavilion Publishing/Mental Health Foundation, 2000

Chapter 11

Working with people with long-term needs

Jo Borrill

Thirty years ago the prospects for most people with long-term mental health needs were bleak – a lifetime of institutionalisation or a marginalised, stigmatised existence on the fringes of society. While there are many concerns about inadequate and inappropriate services and about the continuing stigma surrounding mental health problems, there has undoubtedly been progress and there are reasons to be optimistic about future change.

In thinking about working with people with long-term needs, I have chosen to focus on two areas:

1 developments in treatment

2 methods of preventing relapse.

Underpinning both these developments is the increasing recognition of the importance of self-management, which is complementary to the user-led initiatives described elsewhere in this book.

Developments in Treatment

Medication

For many people with long-term mental health needs, questions about medication – its acceptability, effectiveness, appropriateness – are a central concern. It is clear that people who are prescribed medication vary in their medical and psychological reactions to it. Anti-psychotic drugs, for example, have been experienced by some users as a lifeline, while others have reported devastating effects on their ability to function. It is therefore very important to listen carefully to people's views about their medication and to support them in thinking carefully and constructively about what is best for them.

Most of the drugs which are now prescribed for people with long-term mental health problems work on the chemical messengers (neurotransmitters) in the brain which control how nerve impulses are transmitted. A breakthrough in the development of drugs for people diagnosed with schizophrenia was the discovery that drugs acting on the neurotransmitter dopamine, seemed to be effective in controlling hallucinations, delusions and other active signs of 'psychosis'. This was a considerable improvement compared with the use of general tranquillisers, but these drugs are not without their problems. Many people experience unpleasant side effects such as muscle tremor; 40% of people continue to experience some psychotic 'symptoms', and about 20% of people are not helped at all. It has even been estimated that older drugs such as chlorpromazine may be responsible for up to 40 deaths per year (Kerwin, 1998). There has therefore been considerable interest in the development of new anti-psychotic drugs, such as clozapine, olanzapine, risperidone, which work on different neurotransmitters and appear to have fewer side effects. The key issue now is whether people who would benefit from these new 'atypical' anti-psychotics can get access to them; one survey found that the prescribing of clozapine and risperidone was restricted, largely due to cost (Hogman, 1997).

In the treatment of severe depression similar developments have occurred, with newer drugs being developed such as **fluoxetine (Prozac)** which target specific kinds of neurotransmitter action. There is still some controversy about whether newer anti-depressant drugs are as effective as the older ones (Spigset & Martensson, 1999) and the decision about what kind of drug to take may therefore depend on what side effects a person experiences. Older **'tricyclic' anti-depressants** may produce blurred vision, a dry mouth or problems with concentration, while **newer anti-depressants such as fluoxetine and venlaxafine** sometimes result in increased anxiety, at least initially. It is therefore very important to encourage people to note down any unpleasant side effects and discuss them with their GP.

People diagnosed with **bipolar disorder** – who experience cycles of extreme mood swings – are usually prescribed **lithium chloride**, which has been in use since 1949. Lithium is a potentially toxic drug if taken at too high a level, but reviews of controlled studies have shown that many people benefit from it (Goodwin & Jamison, 1990). It is therefore particularly important that people taking lithium should have full information, to explain what side effects may occur, and why medical checks are important.

However effective a drug may appear to be in a clinical trial, it is only effective in practice if the people receiving it find it acceptable and helpful and continue to take it. One study suggested that up to 80% of people diagnosed with schizophrenia stopped taking their medication at some time (Corrigan *et al*, 1990). At the other extreme, Chaplin and McGuigan (1996) reported that 40% of people prescribed anti-psychotic drugs at one hospital were receiving excessively high doses, and a recent audit of two hospitals showed that almost half the patients were receiving more than one drug at the same time (Wright *et al*, 1998) which increases the risk of unpleasant side effects. People who decide to stop taking medication because of unpleasant side effects may not know about the possible **withdrawal effects**; for example, people who suddenly stop taking anti-depressants may experience nausea, headache, dizziness and even hallucinations.

What is being done to improve this situation?

Since the 1980s there was an increasing realisation that people need to have accurate information about their medication. It is also clear that having some actual control over one's own medication is even more important. Working with people with long-term mental health needs should therefore include helping them to find a way of reviewing and managing their medication. An example of how this can work well is the Medication Review Clinic at the Maudsley Hospital, which offers the opportunity of an independent review and a discussion of alternative treatment strategies. The person with mental health problems participates actively in this process. Preliminary information indicates that about 30% of reviews recommend a change of drug and many suggested an alternative diagnosis. Most importantly, people who attended the clinic and were able to be involved in making decisions about their treatment were more willing to try out new ways of managing their own health (Gray *et al*, 1998).

Non-medical treatments

One of the most significant developments in treatment in the last 20 years has been the increasing use of cognitive therapies for a range of mental health problems. **Cognitive approaches focus on the ways in which a person's thoughts about themselves and their situation can contribute to mental health problems.**

The most well known cognitive approach is **Cognitive Behaviour Therapy (CBT)** which combines established behavioural methods (such as practising new coping skills, learning to face up to frightening situations etc) with an emphasis on changing the negative thought patterns which often prolong mental health problems. CBT is established as an effective form of treatment for many forms of anxiety and depression and can be used alongside medication.

Although not everyone will be helped by cognitive approaches, their particular value for people with long-term mental health problems such as severe depression is that, compared with drug treatment alone, improvements may be maintained for longer after treatment ends (Blackburn *et al*, 1986). Unfortunately, access to cognitive therapies is relatively limited compared with access to medication and people need to know that this kind of help exists in order to be able to ask for it. In order to receive this kind of therapy a person will normally need to get a referral from their GP, usually to a clinical psychologist or a specially-trained psychiatric nurse.

Cognitive therapies are now being used with people diagnosed with schizophrenia who continue to have distressing experiences despite taking medication. The techniques which are used focus on teaching people specific strategies to deal with their symptoms and to cope with broader problems.

A recent study (Tarrier *et al*, 1998) compared CBT with **supportive counselling** and with routine care for people in the community diagnosed with schizophrenia and taking medication. Those people who received CBT showed the greatest improvement in terms of distressing symptoms – a considerable number experienced a reduction of 50% or more. Supportive counselling was better than routine care in this respect but not as helpful as CBT.

However, both CBT and supportive counselling reduced the risk of relapse and the number of days spent in hospital. These results confirm that helping people to develop strategies for managing distressing symptoms can actually reduce their experience of those symptoms; furthermore, showing interest and giving support can make a real difference to a person's quality of life.

Other non-medical approaches include in-depth psychotherapy and various forms of counselling. Long-term psychotherapy is expensive and unlikely to be available to most people, but many GP practices now employ counsellors who can offer support for people going through stressful experiences. Basic counselling skills, such as listening skills, are important for anyone working in mental health, since many service users say that more than any kind of therapy, what they really want is someone to talk to (Faulkner, 1997).

It is also important to consider the person's mental health in the context of their general lifestyle. For example, a recent study reported that brisk regular exercise may be as effective as anti-depressant medication in relieving depression (Blumenthal, 1999).

Relapse Prevention

Identifying the signs of relapse

There is a growing realisation amongst professionals that users of mental health services can often identify particular signs that predict when they are about to become unwell or experience a crisis. These signs are referred to by psychiatrists as **'prodromal' signs (or 'relapse prodromes')**. Pioneering work on identifying early signs of relapse in schizophrenia was carried out by Birchwood and colleagues, based on interviews with people with schizophrenia and their families (Birchwood *et al*, 1989). About two thirds of the people who were interviewed were able to identify signs such as loss of interest, disturbing dreams, or problems with concentration, which tended to appear about a week before an episode of relapse.

Empowering people to identify their own personal 'relapse signatures' is the first stage in helping to avoid relapse; the second stage is for the person to formulate a set of rules or strategies which they can implement when these signs of vulnerability occur. For example, they might learn to use stress-management techniques, or seek increased support or changes in medication.

A similar approach is now being adopted to help people diagnosed with bipolar disorder (manic-depression) identify early signs of relapse. Perry *et al* (1999) reported that teaching people to recognise signs of an impending episode of 'mania' slowed down the rate of relapse and reduced the number of relapse episodes over 18 months, although there was no significant impact on episodes of depression. People also fared better at work and in their social lives as they became more confident in their ability to cope with relapse.

The Manic Depression Fellowship (MDF) has recently developed a user-led course to help people *'develop new strategies, monitor mood states, link thoughts feelings and behaviours, and develop an alertness to mood variations'* (Harris, 1999). This course consists of six sessions, focusing on recognising warning signs, constructing an individual action plan, maintaining support systems, and preparing instructions for others in case of a crisis.

Crisis planning

Even though the risk of relapse can be reduced, people with long-term needs have to face the possibility of future crisis. An important component is having a way of recording their preferred strategy for dealing with an impending crisis, in preparation for a time when they may be unable to communicate their wishes clearly. In the MDF course described above, the final element is the drawing up of 'advance directives', which are a way of informing other people how one would wish to be treated in a crisis. This can include instructions about who to contact, what arrangements to make, as well as views about medication and treatment interventions. By constructing an advance directive a person can reduce their worries about their family or home and can also reduce the possibility of being forced or coerced into receiving an undesirable form of treatment.

This approach has its origins in the idea of a crisis card. Crisis cards were first developed by user-led groups, primarily to enable people to nominate an advocate in a crisis, but they have also been developed in ways which encourage users and professional to work together. Szmukler (1998) described a system of joint crisis planning where people with mental health problems discuss their plans with a professional team, including a facilitator, to mediate between user and professionals. Joint planning produced cards which included information about signs of relapse, helpful/unhelpful interventions, current medication, and other aspects of care. The data collected so far suggests that most people found this process helpful, and use of the card appears to be associated with a reduction in hospital admissions.

Working through families

The attitudes of professionals to the families of people with mental health problems have changed dramatically over the last 30 years. In the 1960s, families were routinely blamed for causing mental health problems and excluded from any role in recovery. At the same time, families who were caring for a person with severe mental illness received little or no emotional support.

However, key research in the 1970s (Brown *et al*, 1972; Vaughn & Leff, 1976) demonstrated that families could help people diagnosed with schizophrenia to stay well for longer, through adopting a particular style of emotional contact (known as 'low expressed emotion'), which avoided criticism or hostility, and was supportive without being 'over-involved'. Later research has demonstrated convincingly that if families are offered training and support in adopting this style of communication then the family member with mental health problems has a much lower risk of relapse (Leff *et al*, 1982), particularly if the contact with the family is kept to a mutually manageable level. Even a brief programme to educate the family about schizophrenia and change their attitudes to the person with schizophrenia can be beneficial (Smith & Birchwood, 1987).

Similarly, we know that social support factors are very important in helping people vulnerable to depression survive the 'ups and downs' of life. Brown and Harris (1978), in their classic study of women in Camberwell, found that women who were employed and women who had 'someone to confide in' were less vulnerable to becoming depressed when experiencing difficult or distressing events in their lives. This leads us to some broader questions about how we can support families and communities to take on this supportive role.

Fadden (1998) has pointed out that there has been relatively little recent research into the needs of family caregivers, yet families do need support. It can be very traumatic for a parent, for example, to see their adult child experiencing difficulties without knowing how to help. According to Fadden, the challenge for the new century is to provide better services for people experiencing psychosis and their families which meet the needs of all involved.

Working in Partnership

It is clear from the work described opposite that when professionals work jointly with users some creative changes in treatment and intervention can occur. An example of this is the Hearing Voices movement, which initially came about through the partnership between the Dutch psychiatrist Marius Romme and one of his clients, who explained her voice-hearing experiences to him and helped design a questionnaire for other voice-hearers. This work showed that hearing voices was a more common experience than expected, and was not just a 'symptom' of schizophrenia. For example, people may hear voices when they are coping with a traumatic event, or when they are facing difficult decisions in their lives. It was also apparent that some people were able to manage their voices, through setting limits to how and when they listened to them. Trying to ignore the voices or use distraction was associated with poorer coping (Romme *et al,* 1992). From this work, general guidelines were developed for working with people who hear voices:

- accept the person's experience of voices
- try to understand the language being used and the feelings being expressed
- help the person talk about their voices, for example by finding local voice-hearer groups, as a way of reducing the fear of voices and developing strategies for managing them.

Conclusions

This selective review of new developments in treatment and relapse prevention has focused particularly on self-management strategies, not just because it is ethically desirable, but because we 'know it makes sense!'

The following summary of points should provide some guidelines for helping people to manage their own mental health over a long period.

- Listen to what people say about their experiences and feelings

- Provide as much information as possible about medication, and encourage people to ask for regular medication reviews, particularly where people are taking more than one drug or are experiencing side effects

- Encourage people to try different strategies for managing 'symptoms', such as negative or disturbing thoughts; treat these as problems to be managed rather than simply as signs of illness

- Find out how people can access specialised help (eg cognitive therapy) if appropriate

- Work with people to identify their personal 'relapse signatures' and to identify which methods of support will prevent or delay relapse

- Help people plan for crises, including the use of crisis cards or advance directives if appropriate

- Help people find constructive ways of relating to friends and families, based on what we know about 'expressed emotion'; remember that families may need support too

- Try to understand what people who hear voices are experiencing, and encourage them to find support through talking to others with similar experiences

- Remember that some people will always be vulnerable; they may need regular counselling, help with employment and accommodation, since 'a suitable living environment can significantly reduce the rate of relapse' (Frude, 1998)

References

Birchwood M., Smith, J., Macmillan, F., Hogg, B., Prasad, R., Harvey, C. & Bering, S. (1989) Predicting Relapse in Schizophrenia; the Development and Implementation of an Early Signs Monitoring System Using Patients and Families as Observers. *Psychological Medicine* **19** 649–656.

Blackburn, I. M., Eunson, K. M. & Bishop, S. (1986) A Two-Year Naturalistic Follow-Up of Depressed Patients Treated With Cognitive Therapy, Pharmacotherapy and a Combination of Both. *Journal of Affective Disorders* **10** 67–75.

Blumenthal, J. (1999) Duke Study: Exercise May Be Just as Effective as Medication for Treating Major Depression. *The Archives of Internal Medicine,* October 25th

Brown, G. W., Birley, J. L. T. & Wing, J. K. (1972) The Influence of Family Life on the Course of Schizophrenic Disorders. *British Journal of Psychiatry* **121** 241–258.

Brown, G. W. & Harris, T. O. (1978) *Social Origins of Depression.* London: Tavistock.

Chaplin, R. & McGuigan, S. (1996) Antipsychotic Dose: From Research to Clinical Practice. *Psychiatric Bulletin* **20** (8) 452–454.

Corrigan, P. W., Liberman, R. P. & Engel, J. D. (1990) From Non-compliance to Collaboration in the Treatment of Schizophrenia. *Hospital & Community Psychiatry* **41** (1) 1203–1211.

Fadden, G. (1998) Family Intervention in Psychosis. *Journal of Mental Health* **7** (2) 115–122.

Faulkner, A. (1997) *Knowing Our Own Minds.* London: The Mental Health Foundation.

Frude, N. (1998) *Understanding Abnormal Psychology.* Oxford: Blackwell.

Goodwin, F. K. & Jamison, K. R. (1990) *Manic-Depressive Illness.* New York: Oxford University Press.

Gray, R., Revely, A., Taylor, D. & Howard, A. (1998) Finding a Treatment to Suit the Patient: the Maudsley Medication Review Clinic. *Mental Health Care* **2** (4) 132–134.

Harris, A. (1999) Crisis Avoidance. *OpenMind* **96** (12).

Hogman, G. (1997) *Is Cost a Factor?* London: National Schizophrenia Fellowship.

Kerwin, R. (1998) *Anti-psychotic Treatments for Schizophrenia.* Paper presented at Mental Health '98, Treatments for Mental Illness: State of the Art. London, Royal College of Physicians, October 1998.

Leff, J., Kuipers, L., Berkowitz, R., Eberlein-Vries, R./ & Sturgeon, D. (1982) A Controlled Trial of Social Intervention of Schizophrenic patients. *British Journal of Psychiatry* **141** 121–134.

Perry, A., Tarrier, N., Morriss, R., McCarthy, E. & Limb, K. (1999) Randomised Controlled Trial of Efficacy of Teaching Patients With Bipolar Disorder to Identify Early Symptoms of Relapse and Obtain Treatment. *British Medical Journal* **318** 149–153.

Romme, M. A. J., Honig, A., Noordhoorn, E. O. & Escher, A. D. (1992) Coping With Hearing Voices: An Emancipatory Approach. *British Journal of Psychiatry* **16** 99–103.

Smith, J. & Birchwood, M. (1987) Specific and Non-specific Effects of Educational Intervention With Families Living With a Schizophrenic Relative. *British Journal of Psychiatry* **150** (649).

Szmukler, G. (1998) *Crisis Cards.* Paper presented at Mental Health 1998, Treatments for Mental Illness: State of the Art. London, Royal College of Physicians, October 1998.

Spigset, O. & Martensson, B. (1999) Drug Treatment of Depression. *British Medical Journal* **318** 1188–1191

Tarrier, N., Yusupoff, L., Kinney, C., McCarthy, E., Gledhill, A., Haddock, G. & Morris, J. (1998) Randomised Controlled Trial of Intensive Cognitive Behaviour Therapy For Patients With Chronic Schizophrenia. *British Medical Journal* **317** 303–307.

Vaughn, C. E. & Leff, J. P. (1976) The Influence of Family and Social Factors on the Course of Psychiatric Patients. *British Journal of Psychiatry* **129** 125–137.

Wright, B., Whitemore, J. & Taylor, D. (1998) *Results of an Audit of Neuroleptic Prescribing at Joyce Green and Maudsley Hospital.* London: Bethlem & Maudsley NHS Trust.

Chapter 12

Strategies for living with mental distress

Alison Faulkner

'We are all the primary experts on our own mental health and about what works for us... we can and should value the coping strategies we have developed for ourselves.'

Faulkner, 1997

This chapter is based on the user-led programme of work at the Mental Health Foundation, a programme that started with the survey reported in *Knowing Our Own Minds (1997)* and continues through the Strategies for Living project funded by the National Lottery Charities Board (due to end in 2000). The work is founded within the increasingly strong demands for change, for freedom of choice and for alternatives to the traditional medical models of treatment coming from service users and user groups. It also attempts to address another concern amongst service users and survivors: that of so often being the passive recipients of research as well as of services.

Here, we describe research undertaken and informed by service users/survivors, and our attempts to redress the balance of power over the research agenda. As pointed out by Mo Hutchison (see **Chapter 2**), *'if users are to regain some control over their lives there needs to be a shift in the balance of power between themselves and mental health professionals'*. We hope that we are making a contribution to that shift in power, both through the strategies and alternatives we are exploring but also through undertaking and promoting user-led research. The aims of the Strategies for Living project are to:

- document and disseminate people's strategies for living with mental distress, through research, publications, newsletters and networks

- promote a holistic approach towards mental health, taking account of people's mental, physical, spiritual and emotional needs

- raise user, carer, professional and public awareness about alternative ways of living and coping with mental distress, including complementary therapies and religious and spiritual beliefs

- encourage and promote user-led research in mental health, enabling service users to set the research agenda and to carry out their own research.

Everyone involved in the project as staff, volunteers, interviewers and participants, has some experience of mental distress and/or of using mental health services. We believe that this is vital in reaffirming our own expertise and in attempting to address the stigma that mental distress invokes.

Knowing Our Own Minds: a survey of how people in emotional distress take control of their lives

Knowing Our Own Minds was a questionnaire survey of people's views and experiences of a range of different treatments, therapies and activities. The research was directed by a steering group of mental health service users, some of whom were members of national user groups, some of local groups. The group decided on the topics to be covered, the structure of the questionnaire and the way in which it was distributed. In the questionnaire, we asked questions about:

- medication and ECT
- complementary therapies
- religious and spiritual beliefs
- hobbies and interests
- talking treatments
- personal coping strategies.

The survey gives us some useful insights into how helpful or unhelpful different treatments and therapies are to people, as well as insight into what people value about the treatments they find helpful. For example, the views about medication reflected in the survey show how very variable the experience of different drugs can be for different people. The views expressed about major tranquillisers were particularly polarised. Just over half of those people who had used them found them 'helpful' or 'helpful at times', yet this was also the group of drugs named as the most damaging, with people complaining about side effects such as confusion, lethargy, and lack of motivation.

The alternative and complementary therapies and strategies covered in the survey were generally experienced as helpful. Many people expressed appreciation of the approach taken by the therapist, the time and attention given to them, or the opportunity to take some control over their own health or lives. Analysis of the comments made by our survey respondents gives us some insight into the aspects people valued or found helpful in these different therapies or activities - and in turn helps us to understand what mental health services might aim for in improving the quality of people's lives.

What do we value or find helpful?

- someone to talk to
- relaxation
- something to occupy my mind
- social support
- expression of feelings

- symptom relief
- structure to the day
- holistic approach
- sense of responsibility
- understanding feelings and behaviour

These were the dominant themes, and different people were able to access or appreciate them through different routes. Relaxation, for example, was a remarkably common theme; people found relaxation from a range of different activities and therapies such as art and creative therapies, complementary therapies (such as massage, yoga), and hobbies and interests, as well as from talking treatments such as counselling or psychotherapy. People valued being treated as a 'whole person', and finding ways of taking control of their lives as well as learning strategies for coping. One of the most common themes expressed was the need for someone to talk to. I have picked out a few of the dominant themes from the research and from our programme of work in the remainder of the chapter, in order to illustrate both the breadth of the work and the direction in which it is going.

Someone to talk to

'Whenever I am in distress, my first thought is "I need someone to talk to".'

'My counsellor was the first person to ever really listen to me, to my problems.'

One of the most common findings of surveys and studies about users' views of psychiatric services, is that people want 'someone to talk to', someone with the time and space to listen to them when they want to talk about their problems, and someone who will believe what they say. Our survey was no different. Most people, in answer to the question 'What do you feel you need when in distress?' responded that they wanted someone to talk to or support from someone. For some people, this was the expression of a need or want, whereas for others it represented their ability to rely on a particular person in their lives, such as a counsellor or therapist, another professional such as GP or CPN, friends, family or other service users.

Whether this often heartfelt plea represents a request for formal 'talking treatments' is a difficult issue to be clear about. In our survey, the issue emerged with particular strength in relation to a time of crisis or distress, which implies the need for crisis and acute services to be able to respond in this way. Mental health services are frequently criticised for their inability to respond to people's needs; staff are often too busy to spend time with patients on wards, and do not see this as a priority in their work.

For the most part, the people in the study were very positive about their experience of 'talking treatments' (counselling or psychotherapy); more people rated this the most helpful treatment overall than any other treatment or therapy they had experienced. There was a general acknowledgement by many that there is insufficient counselling or psychotherapy available for the number of people who want it, and there was evidence in the survey to suggest that access to talking treatments was unequal across different groups of people. The African Caribbean people in the study had less experience of talking treatments than the white people, for example, which supports the findings of other studies, which have found that African-Caribbeans are more often treated with drugs or ECT than their white counterparts.

The follow-up research undertaken as part of the Strategies for Living project is also finding 'someone to talk to' to be a central issue in people's lives. Relationships with others, whether formal (with professionals) or informal (with family or friends), form the basis of many people's strategies for living with mental distress.

Religious and Spiritual Beliefs

'I have a firm belief that God always covers and cares for me whatever life brings. I do not always understand why things happen as they do. But I know whatever we go through God is always there.'

The role of religious or spiritual beliefs in people's lives has rarely been considered in relation to mental health or mental health services, often because of fear (religious imagery can play a part in some people's distress) but also because it is often seen as a minority interest connected predominantly with Black and minority ethnic people or cultures.

Our survey found that religious and spiritual beliefs can be profoundly important to some people, in providing a source of support or comfort and often a powerful sense of meaning in people's lives. There were also some people who had found religious organisations or the people associated with them, to be inflexible or intolerant in response to people's distress, resulting in additional damage or hurt.

This is a theme we have taken forward in the Strategies for Living project, with a seminar in 1998, a publication of people's experiences (*The Courage to Bare Our Souls*, 1999), and the development of a directory of religious and spiritual resources in mental health. It is a subject that has attracted the enthusiasm of a great many people, for whom the issue has remained invisible for far too long:

'I have needed both pills and prayer. I think anti-depressants were crucial to my recovery initially, but my spiritual faith has been a vital "something" extra.'

Personal and Self-help Coping Strategies

'I have found that coping with a major mental illness requires a change in personal attitude. I now lead a much quieter life, go out less and monitor my mood daily.'

'I try hard not to talk back to the voices, I try to shut them out of my mind. I like to listen to music, read and watch TV. Reading is especially good for distracting voices.'

A particularly valuable part of the survey, and one that has helped to point the way forward for us in the Strategies for Living project was the space given to personal and self-help coping strategies. Most of the people in the survey said that they had found their own personal or self-help strategies, and analysis of these open questions gave us the following themes:

- finding ways of motivating myself
  - a structure to the day
  - setting achievable goals
  - maintaining a positive attitude
- getting support from other people
- taking life one day at a time
- looking after myself
- managing my symptoms.

These findings suggest that it can be helpful to think in terms of different kinds or levels of 'coping strategy'. People may have strategies for managing individual difficulties, such as hearing voices or self-harm, they may have overall lifestyle strategies, such as some of those listed above, and they may have strategies for managing in a crisis, such as helpful telephone numbers, crisis cards and advance directives. Strategies can also be many-faceted, as in the self-management of manic depression and training being developed by the Manic Depression Fellowship.

Many people are able to identify ways in which they manage or cope with the mental distress they experience, whether on an individual basis or through self-help or mutual help groups where strategies are shared and discussed. Some people value the treatments or the professionals they come into contact with, whilst others may value the shared strategies from other people experiencing similar problems to their own. Perhaps the most important thing to learn from this research is that **everyone is an individual and everyone's way of coping will be individual.** Enabling a person in distress to find ways of accessing their own strategies will not be based on their diagnosis, but on their interests and motivations as an individual with a unique mental, emotional, physical and spiritual world.

Implications for Services

The implications of the findings from Knowing Our Own Minds for mental health services are many and varied, but are based on the principle that we are all the primary experts on our own mental health, and about what works for us.

If services and mental health workers are able to approach everyone as an individual with their own difficulties, needs and strengths, then it would seem that they are already half way towards adopting a helpful or enabling attitude. Mental health services and the people working in them all too often fall back on the easier approach of categorising people by diagnosis or by their level of service use.

We believe that services should be about *creating environments or opportunities* for:

- people to acknowledge and develop their own strategies
- trying out different activities, strategies, therapies
- listening to people
- learning from each other – self-help and mutual support
- finding appropriate and accessible information
- finding a meaningful structure to the day/week/etc
- developing a holistic approach to mental health.

This is an area that we shall be developing further during our third year, which is focusing on dissemination, through a series of publications and regional seminars.

Self-management

One of the natural developments of our work is to look more closely at self-management of mental distress: what self-management means for people, different forms of self-management, and how to find ways of managing personal distress. We plan to develop a self-management training programme over the next couple of years, in conjunction with the Manic Depression Fellowship.

Self-management, and the idea that we are the experts on our own distress, can sometimes be difficult ideas to understand or believe in, particularly for professionals. However, the principle of self-management is not that people can manage without help, but that we are aware of changes in ourselves and know when to access the help that we need. Professionals can support people in this by acknowledging the strategies we have developed and enabling us to identify others. Being able to recognise when a crisis is approaching and knowing what to do about it does not necessarily mean that you will *avoid* a crisis, but that you have in place the arrangements that you would want to access when you *are* in a crisis situation. The Manic Depression Fellowship suggests a number of stages to the development of self-management techniques:

- **recognition** – the development of awareness about triggers and early warning signs, in order to develop the ability to forward plan

- **action** – the construction of a personal action plan specifying the steps you will take to improve or maintain your mental health, and the circumstances in which you will take them

- **maintenance** – the routine of attending to aspects of our lifestyle to support and maintain mental health

- **crisis management** – the planning in advance of a crisis, with the development of an 'advance directive'.

Following their publication *Inside Out: a guide to self-management of manic depression* (1996), MDF has developed a user-led training course which runs through a number of stages in the development of self-management strategies.

Self-management may not always be easy, but it can be an empowering experience to take control of your own distress. For me, self-management requires a level of honesty with myself and others which is sometimes difficult to achieve. It means accepting certain limitations (as well as strengths!) about myself, learning that it helps to check things out with people sometimes, and learning that it is not a failure to use a service in a crisis, but is actually a vital part of managing that crisis. It has been empowering to develop a number of different sources of help, which make it more likely that I will be able to avoid hospital admission in the future.

Other organisations who have developed self-management techniques are the Hearing Voices Network and the National Self-Harm Network, both of which have developed strategies to manage fairly specific experiences. There are many other self-management strategies however, as our research at Strategies for Living has found, and we hope to raise awareness of these as the third year of the project proceeds.

User-led Research

One of the fundamental principles of the Strategies for Living project is to conduct and support user-led research. By 'user-led research' we mean research in which service users get the opportunity to decide on the issues and questions to be looked at, as well as to design and carry out the research. Most research in the field of mental health is carried out on people with mental health problems, does not include us and very often does not address the questions or issues we believe to be important. We have found that people often feel more able to open up to others who have had similar experiences; there can be a sense of empathy, understanding and of being believed or validated. These ideas are beginning to gain ground within the mental health and research fields. The User-Focused Monitoring Team at the Sainsbury Centre for Mental Health is another example of service users working with other service users – in this case to get feedback on mental health services.

With the Research Support Network, we have been supporting six small research projects run by service users/user groups in different parts of the country. Each of these is on a subject embraced by the themes of the Strategies for Living project; for example, the giving and receiving of massage, auricular acupuncture, peer support through drop-ins, and the experience of Moslem men attending mosque.

Becoming actively involved in research can be liberating, can increase our self-confidence and can give us the chance to affect the shape of mental health services in the future. Research can also be a valuable service evaluation or monitoring tool, can find out information about people's needs or experiences, and can contribute to the ever-growing focus on service quality and evidence-based medicine. The value of service users gathering this sort of information is that they can be seen to be independent of those services in a way that the professionals within them cannot. People using a service are often afraid to criticise it to people involved in providing it, for fear of the service being withdrawn or of other difficult consequences. We believe that evidence gathered by, with and for service users/survivors is crucial to the development of more appropriate, accessible and acceptable services.

References and further reading

Alexander, B. (1993) *The Place of Complementary Therapies in Mental Health: A User's Experiences and Views.* Nottingham Patients' Council Support Group & Nottingham Advocacy Group.

Beresford, P. & Wallcraft, J. (1997) Psychiatric System Survivors and Emancipatory Research: Issues, Overlaps and Differences. In: C. Barnes & G. Mercer (Eds) *Doing Disability Research.* Leeds: The Disability Press.

Faulkner, A. (1998) Experts by Experience. *Mental Health Nursing* **18** (4) 6–8.

Faulkner, A. (1997) *Knowing Our Own Minds.* London: The Mental Health Foundation.

Faulkner, A. Wallcraft, J., Nicholls, V., Blazdell, J. & Treitel, R. (1998) The Right to Ask the Questions. *OpenMind* **91** (14).

Fernando, S. (1995) Professional Interventions: Therapy and Care. In: S. Fernando (Ed) *Mental Health in a Multi-ethnic Society.* London: Routledge.

Harris, A. (1999) Crisis Avoidance. *OpenMind* **96**.

Lindow, V. (1994) *Self-Help Alternatives to Mental Health Services.* London: Mind Publications.

Manic Depression Fellowship (1996) *Inside Out: A Guide to Self-management of Manic Depression.* London: Manic Depression Fellowship.

Mental Health Foundation (1999) *The Courage to Bare Our Souls.* London: MHF.

Mental Health Foundation (1999) *The DIY Guide to Survivor Research.* London: MHF.

Mental Health Foundation (1995) *Mental Health in Black & Minority Ethnic People: The Fundamental Facts.* London: MHF.

Neate, P. (Ed) User Focused Research (Special Issue). *Research Matters. Community Care,* August 1998.

Read, J. & Wallcraft, J. (1992) *Guidelines For Empowering Users of Mental Health Services.* London: Mind/COHSE.

Rogers, A., Pilgrim, D. & Lacey, R. (1993) *Experiencing Psychiatry: Users' Views of Services.* London: Mind Publications.

Rose, D. (1996) *Living in the Community.* London: The Sainsbury Centre for Mental Health.

Rose, D., Ford, R., Lindley, P. & Gawith, L. (1998) *In Our Experience: User-Focused Monitoring of Mental Health Services in Kensington & Chelsea and Westminster Health Authority.* London: Sainsbury Centre for Mental Health.

Wallcraft, J. (1998) *Healing Minds.* London: The Mental Health Foundation.

Wallcraft, J. (1999) Complementary Therapies. *Mental Health Care* **21** (10) 351–354.

Wood, H. (1994) *What Do Service Users Want From Mental Health Services?* Report to the Audit Commission, compiled by Helen Wood. London: Audit Commission.

I'm Dancing with Damaged Wings

When a wind of chaos blows through our lives
It pulls meaning apart
And in the aftermath we sit and wonder
How do you mend a broken heart?

A saddened chuckle echoes through the darkness
It's a survival instinct that we know
And we wonder
How did we lose sight of our world view?
The ideology we held so close?

Somehow our dreams slipped through shaking hands
How can we fit all the pieces together again?
Reaching out for someone,
Someone special to hold onto.

But how do we trust
When experience has taught us so much about suspicion?
How do we love
When we have been hurt so badly?
Which turning do we take on the road
forward from here?

A 'madman' tries to compose himself
So that he can fit in once more with the crowd
He tries hard to make the mask fit
But it's not easy keeping a stiff upper lip
When there's so much to express
So much confusion and bewilderment
At being alone in this hostile world.
When a storm of people blow through our lives

They take, dictate, and leave us drained,
And in the aftermath we sit and wonder
How do we fill this emptiness again?

We tried to trust
Afraid of being alone on an island
We tried to love
Afraid that the wound would hurt too deeply
And sometimes we wish
That we were brave enough to try again.

A 'madperson' tries to be at one with the crowd
But you can't hide fearful eyes
The years of being singled out,
And you can't hide the worry lines
That run across your face
As you take your place in the competitive day.

But memories haunt in the deep of the night
Leaving the longing to open up and cry
And to understand the experiences
That changed the meaning of our lives,
We are damaged
But those experiences have made us wise,
Yes, we can be strong this time.

Frank Bangay, March 1992

Chapter 13

Understanding relationships

Steve Onyett

The central importance of effective working relationships between service users and staff has been highlighted by a wide variety of sources. It is central to effective engagement, assessment, planning, clinical risk-management and a collaborative approach to the use of medication and other therapeutic interventions. Effective relationships may also serve to moderate some of the negative ways in which mental health services respond to people experiencing the effects of social inequalities. If authentic relationships are to be established then both parties will need to understand as fully as possible the social context in which they operate, the realities of the power dynamics between them and the contradictory imperatives of care and control that operate on staff. This in turn argues for a more reflective and politically informed approach to working with disadvantaged people with severe and long-term mental health problems. This needs to be inculcated through training and evaluation, and supported by one's peers and managers over the long term.

There is an increasingly explicit emphasis on the central importance of effective working relationships between users and staff as the essential bedrock of mental health services for people with severe and complex mental health problems. Although this emphasis on effective relationships is intuitively obvious, services often do not operate *as if* effective relationships between staff and users were important. The achievement of such ordinary relationships may require extra-ordinary skill, and important contextual factors need to be taken into account when considering how the relationship will be formed, maintained and understood.

A broad range of research on innovations in provision for people with severe mental health problems highlights the centrality of effective relationships between staff and users. At service-organisational level the development of case management highlights the need for case managers to work alongside users rather than merely assessing their needs and then 'brokering' inputs from a variety of other provider agencies. Mueser *et al's* (1998) review of 75 case-management studies described an evolution of models over time from case management through to assertive community treatment. Case management emerged as patients left closing long-stay psychiatric hospitals as a means to connect them to required services through a brokerage approach. The Accreditation Council for Psychiatric Facilities (1976) provided a comprehensive description of case management:

> *'Case management services are activities aimed at linking the service system to a consumer and at co-ordinating the various system components to achieve a successful outcome...Case management is essentially a problem-solving function designed to ensure continuity of service and to overcome systems rigidity, fragmented service, misutilisation of certain facilities, and inaccessibility'*

The limitations of this role became evident when experience showed that case managers needed to use a high level of clinical skills in order to engage people in care, assess their needs and then intervene effectively. Thus clinical models of case management were developed. While the combination of clinical and brokerage skills was effective for many people with mental health problems, those who had the most severe health and social care needs, and who were high users of services, required a more intensive approach. Leonard Stein, the originator of assertive community treatment in the US argued that brokerage was effective only insofar as there were resources to deploy and agencies with an interest in collaborating (Stein, 1992). As this is usually absent, mental health workers had to be able to act as direct providers. Assertive community treatment and intensive case management therefore developed to shift the focus of care from hospital settings back into the community. Mueser *et al* (1998) concluded that these more intensive home-based approaches are effective in reducing time in hospital but that their impact on psychosocial functioning is limited. A more clinically oriented approach appeared to be needed. The 'strengths' approach is such a model and is founded on six general principles (Rapp & Wintersteen, 1989):

1. focus on individual strengths rather than pathology

2. interventions are based on the principle of user self-determination

3. assertive outreach is the preferred mode of intervention

4. people with long-term and severe mental health problems can continue to learn, grow and change and can be assisted to do so

5. resource acquisition goes beyond traditional mental health services and actively mobilises resources for the entire community; the community is defined as a resource and not as an obstacle

6. the case manager-user relationship is primary and essential.

This emphasis is not new. Nearly a generation ago, Intagliata (1982) stated that the 'most influential aspect of the case management process is the quality of personal commitment that the case managers develop towards their clients'. What is significant is the way in which this key ideological strand has endured and is now supported by a body of research evidence.

From a user perspective (Beeforth *et al,* 1994) evaluations of British case management have stressed the importance of effective relationships. In the US, McGrew *et al* (1996) found that users who were asked about the features of assertive community treatment they liked best most frequently highlighted the helping relationship. Users highlighting such non-specific aspects of the service reported most satisfaction.

Murray *et al* (1997) also provide an example of the importance of effective relationships in providing an acceptable service. They found that, compared with professional staff, community support workers were more likely to be active in those areas of provision that users rated as most important. This included emotional support, assistance with housing, informal daycare, household tasks, and finance. Users often felt that as a result these workers had been instrumental in keeping them out of hospital. **Community support workers were rated by users as being significantly more available, more understanding of their needs, and more honest and open when compared with professional staff.** The community support workers spent more time than professional staff in direct contact with service users.

If we are concerned that users should want to stay working effectively with services then clearly their satisfaction with services is a very significant outcome. However, there has also been a resurgence in interest in the therapeutic alliance between users and staff as a medium for achieving other positive outcomes. Working alliances may be slow and hard to achieve, but reap the benefits of increased adherence to medication regimes, the need for less medication and better outcomes in terms of symptomatology, quality of life and satisfaction with mental health treatment (Frank & Gunderson, 1990; Solomon *et al,* 1995; Gehrs & Goering, 1994).

Long-standing working alliances are also required to achieve a shared understanding of the subjective *meaning* of phenomena experienced by service users diagnosed as psychotic. Such appreciations are critical to understanding the experience of psychosis from the perspective of service users, and the success of innovative psychological approaches to coping with hallucinations and delusions. In introducing a special section in the *Journal of Mental Health* on key advances in psychosocial approaches to psychosis, Birchwood (1998) made the point that *'what unites them is a firm focus upon the person with psychosis as an active agent, searching for meaning and control over psychosis and the survival of the self'*.

A key contextual factor for both users and staff in the UK is the dominant Government policy rhetoric concerning risk to users and the general public. In 1999 the-then UK Secretary of State for Health, Frank Dobson, announced that 'Community care has failed', following a series of homicide inquiries that highlighted the shortcomings of community mental health services. In reality there is no evidence of an increase in the numbers of homicides committed by people with severe mental health problems, and indeed there was a decline in their contribution to the total number of homicides committed in England and Wales between 1957 and 1995 (Taylor & Gunn, 1999). However, the subsequent *National Service Framework for Mental Health in the UK* (Department of Health, 1999) stressed the importance of effective engagement through assertive community treatment, and effective risk assessment and management, principally as a way of reducing suicide rates. While there is never room for complacency on this topic, it is also true that the impact of techniques for risk assessment need to be seen in their proper place. As Morgan (1997) notes:

'Risk factors are somewhat like weather prediction: better at providing an overall picture than a guarantee that we can be sure of what will happen in any specific situation'.

In light of this he concludes:

'Perhaps our most appropriate approach should be to refine and evaluate our basic clinical skills. Suicide rates might well then look after themselves'.

The *Report of the Confidential Inquiry into Homicides and Suicides by Mentally Ill People* (1996) was also clear about the central importance of relationships:

> '*Skills in developing a rapport with people who are seriously mentally ill or mentally disordered require special training and considerable experience... Although it was evident that regular contact had been made with most patients prior to the death, we were concerned that the time for one-to-one contact, where skills in developing a therapeutic relationship and opportunity for listening to the patient might be used were very limited... Audit programmes should address the extent and quality of direct staff: patient contact*'

Dvoskin and Steadman (1994) also showed that intensive case management can reduce violence where case managers have low caseloads, 24-hour availability, and the skills that allow them to work with medical, social and legal systems.

Often the success of assertive approaches in producing better outcomes has been attributed to improvements in the users' adherence to prescribed medication regimes. This underpins the UK Government's apparent conviction that compulsory treatment orders are likely to be necessary in order to reduce the risk of harm to users and the general public.

However, in practice the most promising approaches to improving adherence to medication regimes place great emphasis on examining the users' own conceptualisation of their difficulties and their beliefs about the merits and demerits of taking medication (Kemp *et al*, 1998; Smith *et al*, 1999). These approaches stress the users' role as active agents in their own treatment, and employs techniques such as motivational interviewing (Rollnick & Miller, 1995) to help users resolve their ambivalence about a given course of action, in the context of a balanced power-relationship between users and staff. In practice, this power relationship may become contravened when the model is adapted to place the practitioners in a more active, expert role (Perkins & Repper, 1999).

The diverse sources above highlight the need for staff to be skilled in achieving and developing relationships with users in which the user feels they are an active agent in their care and treatment. So if the challenge is for services to promote a relationship between the user and the practitioner in which they become real people to each other, and where the user perceives the practitioner as someone who is soon able to help them on their own terms, how might this be achieved?

The Challenge of Giving People What They Want

Working to agendas the users set themselves, respecting the importance of those factors that users themselves deem important in describing their situation, and providing a choice of options for making things better are likely to promote more effective involvement in services and thus positive outcomes. For example, Repper *et al* (1994) found that effective working alliances were promoted by proactively offering practical support and assistance.

An intention to work in this way implies a specific ideology of care among staff that forms an important part of the context of relationship formation. Perkins and Repper (1998) review a number of the most dominant ideologies of care operating within mental health services and conclude that ultimately they need to be judged against the extent to which they promote relationships in which *'the person is facilitated in living the life they wish to lead and achieving their own goals... (p24).... Client choice and self-determination are at the heart of effective relationships (p29)'*. The principle of self-determination, also a cornerstone of the strengths model of case management described above (Rapp & Wintersteen, 1989) should not be confused with the 1980s culture of individualism, or the human potential movement of the 1970s. It is not assumed that anyone can be what they want to be if only they take responsibility for themselves and their lives. This too easily equates with blaming those experiencing enduring social inequalities for their own disadvantages. Self-determination is concerned with maximising the power of

users and carers in decision-making concerning their lives,
ensuring that they are able to exercise choice wherever
possible and developing a collaborative approach to the core
tasks of working together.

Honesty and Power

Self-determination involves users making choices, which in
turn requires the power to make decisions that workers may
consider wrong-headed. Perkins and Repper (1998) assert
that workers must be prepared to allow users to make such
decisions, intervening only where the worker's 'duty of care'
to avoid harm to others or the user is invoked. Many users
are motivated towards avoiding involvement with services,
while at the same time staff and their managers feel they have
a duty of care to protect them from harm and effect some
therapeutic benefit. The obvious example is when individuals
are a danger to themselves or others and the practitioner has
to arrange a formal assessment for their removal to a more
controlling environment (such as an acute ward, if no better
alternative exists). The aim of continuous and in-depth
involvement with users is to stop such situations arising.
However, such events are sometimes unavoidable and users
should have access to an independent advocate who will
safeguard their interests. Although the practitioner should be
working on behalf of users, ultimately they lack the
independence from service systems necessary for advocacy
work, particularly if they hold budgetary or resource
rationing responsibilities. However, practitioners may still
have a role in helping the user identify an advocate to act on
their behalf.

Although the relationship between the practitioner and
user is of paramount importance, the relationship between
them is not 'normal' in the way that one might have a
relationship with a friend, relative, or colleague. Professional
staff always have power over users and it is important to
acknowledge this. Good and professional practice is about
recognising this power and avoiding its abuse by making the
relationship as collaborative as possible. This involves mental

health workers fully appreciating the context they find themselves in as workers and particularly the contradictory imperatives of care and control that operate upon them. This could be achieved through direct education about their responsibilities, group work aimed at consciousness raising, and examining ethnographic research that examines these issues, and their implications for the socialisation and practices of staff. A good example would be the excellent study of psychiatric nursing by Handy (1990).

On the basis of this understanding, staff are in a good position to realistically communicate their role to those users where issues of social control may arise. In this way the user is in a better position to exercise choice about how to handle the relationship. In practice, I have found it is rare for users to reject the relationship on these grounds. Rather, it offers a sense of containment, or only serves to confirm what was known by the user already. It also provides the opportunity for collaborative planning concerning crisis and relapse so that the user has exercised maximum control over those situations where, if and when it happens, they are not as in control as they would like to be.

The same rigour concerning honesty and choice can be applied to all other aspects of the user's care and treatment, for example regarding medication and its side effects, psychosocial interventions, and options for housing, work and leisure.

Team Working

It is a paradox that perhaps the most important aspect of teams is the extent to which they are able to promote successful individual relationships between clients and staff. This is suggested by the disappointing outcomes of case management (or 'keyworking' under the UK system) when operated merely as a means of service co-ordination and follow-up outside of a multidisciplinary team context (Franklin *et al,* 1987; Marshall *et al,* 1995; Tyrer *et al,* 1995).

A key element of team working is the way the team provides a vehicle for an ideology that promotes effective relationships as described above. For example, it is important that the team as a whole inculcates among its members a realistic sense of what a valued outcome might be for the people it serves, and over what period. While advocates of a recovery model have rightly underlined the possibility of full recovery of valued roles for people diagnosed with psychoses, and the importance of instilling hope and optimism, it is equally true that change is often very slow, and that crises, relapse and deterioration are also commonplace. If the team is too orientated towards notions of recovery and discharge there is a danger that staff can become demoralised when, despite their efforts, little or no change occurs. To be effective allies of people with severe and long-term mental health problems, staff need to be able to support a person through the bad times as well as the good *'in order to help them to do the things they want and live the life they want to live'* (Perkins & Repper, 1998). Perkins and Repper (1998) argued that staff need to find a range of sources of reward from their work, such as the privilege of knowing people whose lives are so unusual, the innovation required to achieve the access to services, resources and relationships that they desire, helping people to live with their problems, and taking pleasure in the satisfaction that people derive from managing to achieve something they really want after years of effort. Onyett *et al* (1997) describe the features of team management and leadership that promote such user-centred, outcome-orientated team practice.

Other Key Contextual Factors

This has been a very selective look at some of the less obvious but key contextual issues relevant to developing effective relationships. Others are discussed below:

- **The need to work in the user's own physical and social contexts**

- **The impact of a lack of resources on reducing choice and increasing coercion**: Where there is a chronic lack of

Looking to the Future © Pavilion Publishing/Mental Health Foundation, 2000

adequate and appropriate provision services become crisis-driven, overly concerned with social control, and delivered in a manner that precludes the development of good quality relationships and collaborative work with service users. As Diamond (1996) noted: *'When effective community based treatments are available, the effectiveness of community based coercion increases but the need for such coercion is less'*

- **The personal qualities and skills required to achieve effective relationships:** Williams *et al* (1994) did not find educational level to be predictive of success when recruiting to a well-established and successful case management service in California. They instead emphasised attitudes and interpersonal abilities such as optimism about the potential for service users to change, and flexibility.

  It is also important that staff have specific clinical expertise, for example, in doing a broad enough assessment to ensure that psychosocial interventions are not set up to fail. For example, Wykes and Carson (1996) stress the importance of being able to differentiate social anxiety from social skills deficits. They estimate that the former may hamper rehabilitation in up to a quarter of patients and requires a very different response to that required to rectify a skills deficit. Similarly there will often be a need to assess and evaluate cognitive deficits before implementing interventions

- **The need to communicate simply about complex situations:** Functional analysis is a framework for considering assessment as an ongoing collaborative project between users and staff (Owens & Ashcroft, 1982). It is not tied to any particular psychological theory but looks for circularity in the way people function and focuses on these feedback loops as targets for intervention. As with a behavioural analysis, functional analysis requires a clear specification of the presenting problems and a classification of the various events and variables that surround them according to:

  - whether they serve to increase or decrease the probability of a problem
  - whether they occur before or after a problem.

However, the variables of a functional analysis need not be specified in behavioural terms, and the ABC analysis is applied repeatedly in order to discover the circularity that is maintaining the situation in its present state. The practitioner places more emphasis on whether the formulation has explanatory power, rather than whether it is 'true'. On the basis of a working hypothesis, the user and their worker can attempt to change the presenting problems by manipulating either the environment that precedes the problem or by attempting to change its consequences, or attempting to change their own behavioural, cognitive or affective responses. The development of a formulation using this approach is like an experiment undertaken by the user and worker as collaborators. It can be useful to literally build a picture of what may be going on, incorporating or removing links over time. This systematic approach to the way people think, act and feel helps establish a developing picture of what is happening. The resulting functional analysis and the interventions that flow from it are complex but transparent and unique to the user

- **Awareness of the effects of social inequalities experienced by service users:** Clearly this will be easier if they have similar cultural and economic backgrounds. However, even where this is not the case some of the effects of social inequality, such as the tendency to over-prescribe anti-psychotics to Black clients, can be ameliorated when efforts to engage clients are rated higher (Segal *et al*, 1996). The effects of social inequalities have recently been reviewed by Pilgrim and Rogers (1999).

Clinical Governance as a Way Forward

Mental health services in the UK will be delivered within a 'clinical governance' framework *'through which the NHS organisations are responsible for continuously improving the quality of their services and safeguarding high standards of care by creating an environment in which excellence in clinical care will flourish'* (Department of Health, 1998). In theory this should improve the context for developing effective relationships between staff and users. The Government's White Paper on quality (ibid) places the experience of users and carers at the very centre of a new National Performance Framework. There will also be greater emphasis on evidence-based practice to achieve clinical effectiveness, specific standards, improved professional self-regulation, and a strong emphasis on continuous professional development to ensure the workforce is 'fit for purpose'. However, Pilgrim (1999) points out that for the potential of this new regime to be realised, greater clarity and honesty needs to be achieved about the function of mental health services. The 'mental hospitals' had essentially three functions: long-term accommodation, social control and ameliorative treatment. Assuming these functions under some benign heading of 'community care' is confusing, and obscures the contradictory imperatives that pertain to every level of the organisations involved in mental health care. These functions need to be kept analytically separate when evaluating the success of clinical governance.

Contradictions between care and control need to be made explicit, so that the aims of proposed actions can be transparent and tested against the available evidence-base. This might, for example, underline the need to focus on the issues involved in developing collaborative relationships with users judged to be most at risk, using the considerable international experience available, before seeking to introduce compulsory treatment orders which may well further alienate the very group the services are aiming to engage, thereby increasing the risk to those individuals and the general public of which they form a part.

Smith (1992) drew parallels between approaches to quality assurance in industry and the application of similar models to human services. She concluded that the failure to implement effective quality assurance strategies stemmed from an over-emphasis on monitoring and inspection, rather than an emphasis on partnership with users, and workers exerting control over quality-related activities.

Krupa *et al* (1992) in describing their experience of implementing training to support rehabilitation in a hospital setting, also stressed the need for honesty about the implications of change. This gives workers a greater sense of control over this key quality-assurance process. It clearly should not be assumed that trainees will be willing and eager recipients. Training implies change, which will have a personal impact on staff in terms of their employment status, job satisfaction and self-esteem. They recommend explicitly stating benefits for individuals and the system, integrating old with new knowledge and facilitating open discussion and debate. Involving enthusiastic and credible advocates of change can be helpful along with concrete and familiar case examples that will help root the training in the experience of users. A more direct approach is to involve users in the training. Involving users as trainers can help to highlight the tensions involved in promoting self-determination in a risk-averse society, and ensures that the issues are struggled with realistically, and across disciplines. Employing users as staff members also provides effective role models for both users and staff on how these tensions can be resolved. Case management services are increasingly employing current or ex-service users in case-management roles (Sherman & Porter, 1991; Nikkell *et al*, 1992; Williams *et al*, 1994) and randomised trials find them to be just as effective as case managers as are non-service users (Solomon & Draine, 1995).

Similar principles can be applied to service evaluation as part of the quality-assurance process. Pilgrim (1997) expressed concern about the failure to base quality assurance processes on those aspects of change that are most valued by service users (such as improved quality of life), and a bias towards randomised controlled trials as the basis for evidence based practice. Such methods usually fail to represent the experience of service users and require practices that are a poor analogue of usual practice. There are now well-established approaches to service evaluation, such as *User Focused Monitoring* (Rose *et al*, 1998) which employ users to talk to other users about their experience of services using specific protocols.

Clinical governance holds much promise to improve mental health service provision in the UK. However, its implementation will require an acknowledgement of the importance of organisational culture and ideology, and the training, leadership and approaches to evaluation required to shape it (Scally & Donaldson, 1998). Ultimately, the achievement of relationships in which users can shape their own destiny should be the standard against which such innovations are judged.

(This chapter was previously published in 'Psychiatric Rehabilitation Skills' under the title *Understanding relationships in context as a core competence for psychiatric rehabilitation*.

Psychiatric Rehabilitation Skills has kindly given permission for its use here.)

References

Accreditation Council for Psychiatric Facilities (1976) *Principles of Accreditation of Community Mental Health Service Programs.* Joint Commission on Accreditation of Hospitals.

Beeforth, M., Conlon, E. & Graley, R. (1994) *Have We Got Views For You.* London: Sainsbury Centre for Mental Health.

Birchwood, M. (1998) New Directions in the Psychosocial Approach to Psychoses. *Journal of Mental Health* **7** (2) 111–114.

Confidential Inquiry into Homicides and Suicides by Mentally Ill People (1996) *Report of the Confidential Inquiry into Homicides and Suicides by Mentally Ill People.* London: Royal College of Psychiatrists.

Department of Health (1998) *A First Class Service.* London: The Stationery Office.

Department of Health (1999) *National Service Framework for Mental Health: Modern Standards & Service Models.* London: The Stationery Office.

Diamond, R. J. (1996) Coercion and Tenacious Treatment in the Community: Applications to the Real World. In: D. L. Dennis and J. Monahan (Eds) *Coercion and Aggressive Community Treatment: A new Frontier in Mental Health Law.* New York: Plenum Press.

Dvoskin, J. A. & Steadman, H. J. (1994) Using Intensive Case Management To Reduce Violence By Mentally Ill Persons in the Community. *Hospital and Community Psychiatry* **45** (7) 679–684.

Frank, A. F. & Gunderson, J. G. (1990) The Role of the Therapeutic Alliance in the Treatment of Schizophrenia. *Archives of General Psychiatry* **47** 228–236.

Franklin, J. L., Solovitz, B., Mason, M., Clemons, J. R. & Miller, G. (1987) An Evaluation of Case Management. *American Journal of Public Health* **77** 674–678.

Gehrs, M. & Goering, P. (1994) The Relationship Between the Working Alliance and Rehabilitation Outcomes of Schizophrenia. *Psychosocial Rehabilitation Journal* **18** 43–54.

Handy, J. (1990) *Occupational Health in a Caring Profession.* Aldershot: Avebury.

Intagliata, J. (1982) Improving the Quality of Care For the Chronically Mentally Disabled: the Role of Case Management. *Schizophrenia Bulletin* **8** (4) 655–673.

Kemp, R., Kirov, G., Everitt, B., Hayward, P. & David, A. (1998) Randomised Controlled Trial of Compliance Therapy. *British Journal of Psychiatry* **172** 413–419.

Klinkenberg, W. D. & Calsyn, R. J. (1996) Predictors of Receipt of Aftercare and Recidivism Among Persons With Severe Mental Illness: a Review. *Psychiatric Services* **47** (5) 487–496.

Krupa, T., Eastabrook, S., Blake, P. & Goering, P. (1992) Lessons Learned: Introducing psychiatric Rehabilitation in a Multidisciplinary Hospital. *Psychosocial Rehabilitation Journal* **15** (3) 29–36.

Marshall, M., Lockwood, A., & Gath, D. (1995) Social Services Case-management For Long-term Mental Disorders: a Randomised Controlled Trial. *The Lancet* **345** 409–12.

McGrew, J. H., Wilson, R. G. & Bond, G. R. (1996) Client Perspectives on Helpful Ingredients of Assertive Community Treatment. *Psychiatric Rehabilitation Journal* **19** (3) 13–21.

Morgan, H. G. (1997) Management of Suicide Risk. *Psychiatric Bulletin* **21** 214–216.

Mueser, K. T., Bond, G.R., Drake, R. E. & Resnick, G. (1998) Models of Community Care For Severe Mental Illness: A Review of Research on Case Management. *Schizophrenia Bulletin* **24** (1) 38–73.

Murray, A., Shepherd, G., Onyett, S. R. & Muijen, M. (1997) *More Than a Friend: The Role of Support Workers in Community Mental Health Services.* London: Sainsbury Centre for Mental Health.

Nikkel, R. E., Smith, G. & Edwards, D. (1992) A Consumer-operated Case Management Project. *Hospital and Community Psychiatry* **43** (6) 577–579.

Onyett, S. R., Standen, R. & Peck, E. (1997) The Challenge of Community Mental Health Team Management. *Health and Social Care in the Community* **5** (1) 40–47.

Owens, R. G. & Ashcroft, J. B. (1982) Functional Analysis in Applied Psychology. *British Journal of Clinical Psychology* **21** 181–9.

Perkins, R. & Repper, J. M. (1998) Principles of Working With People Who Experience Serious Mental Health Problems. In: C. Brooker & J. Repper (Eds) *Serious Mental Health Problems in the Community: Policy, Practice and Research.* London: Bailliere Tindall Limited.

Perkins, R. & Repper, J. M. (1999) Compliance or Informed Choice. *Journal of Mental Health* **8** (2) 117–129.

Pilgrim, D. (1997) Some Reflections on 'Quality' and 'Mental Health'. *Journal of Mental Health* **6** (6) 567–576.

Pilgrim, D. (1999). Making the Best of Clinical Governance. *Journal of Mental Health* **8** (1) 1–2.

Pilgrim, D. & Rogers, A. (1999) *A Sociology of Mental Health and Illness.* Buckingham: Open University Press.

Rapp, C. A. & Wintersteen, R. (1989) The Strengths Model of Case Management: Results from Twelve Demonstrations. *Psychosocial Rehabilitation Journal* **13** (1) 23–32.

Repper, J., Ford, R. & Cooke, A. (1994) How Can Nurses Build Relationships With People Who Have Severe and Long-term Mental Health Problems? Experience of Case Managers and Their Clients. *Journal of Advanced Nursing* **19** 1096–1104.

Rollnick, S. & Miller, W. R. (1995) What is Motivational Interviewing? *Behavioural and Cognitive Psychotherapy* **23** 325–334.

Rose, D., Ford, R., Lindley, P. & Gawith, L. (1998) *In Our Experience: User-Focused Monitoring of Mental Health Services in Kensington & Chelsea and Westminster Health Authority.* London: Sainsbury Centre for Mental Health.

Scally, G. & Donaldson, L. J. (1998) Clinical Governance and the Drive For Quality Improvement in the New NHS in England. *British Medical Journal* **317** 61–65.

Segal, S. P., Bola, J. R. & Watson, M. A. (1996) Race, Quality of Care, and Antipsychotic Prescribing Practices in Psychiatric Emergency Services. *Psychiatric Services* **47** (3) 282–285.

Sherman, P. S. & Porter, R. (1991) Mental Health Consumers as Case Management Aides. *Hospital and Community Psychiatry* **42** (5) 494–498.

Smith, H. (1992) Quality in Community Care: Moving Beyond Mediocrity. *Journal of Mental Health* **1** 207–217.

Smith, J. A., Hughes, I. & Budd, R. J. (1999) Non-compliance With Anti-psychotic Depot Medication: Users' Views on Advantages and Disadvantages. *Journal of Mental Health* **8** (3) 287–296.

Solomon, P. & Draine, J. (1995) The Efficacy of a Consumer Case Management Team: Two-year Outcomes of a Randomised Trial. *Journal of Mental Health Administration* **22** (2) 135–145.

Solomon, P., Draine, J. & Delaney, M. A. (1995) The Working Alliance and Consumer Case Management. *Journal of Mental Health Administration* **22** (2) 126–134.

Stein, L. I. (1992) On the Abolishment of the Case Manager. *Health Affairs Fall* 172–177.

Taylor, P. J. & Gunn, J. (1999) Homicides By People With Mental Illness: myth and reality. *British Journal of Psychiatry* **174** 9–14.

Tyrer, P., Morgan, J., Van Horn, E., Jayakody, M., Evans, K., Brummell, R., White, T., Baldwin, D., Harrison-Read, P. & Johnson, T. (1995) A Randomised Controlled Study of Close Monitoring of Vulnerable Psychiatric Patients. *The Lancet* **345** 756–59.

Williams, M. L., Forster, P., McCarthy, G. D. & Hargreaves, W. A. (1994) Managing Case Management: What Makes it Work? *Psychosocial Rehabilitation Journal* **18** (1) 49–60.

Wykes, T. & Carson, J. (1996) Psychosocial Factors in Schizophrenia: Implications For Rehabilitation and Community Care. *Current Opinion in Psychiatry* **9** 68–72.

Chapter 14

The soul of psychiatry

Roger Moss

What makes the care of people with mental health problems tick? Where is the heartbeat of this work? Are the spiritual aspects of people within or outside the remit of mental health work? Can we really do much to restore the soul of individuals if, as mental health workers, as teams, as caring professions, we have no way of attending to the needs of our own soul?

1. Soul

If psychiatry ever had a soul, it seems to have lost it.

In a literal sense psychology is the study of the soul, and psychiatry the treatment or healing of the soul. 'Psyche' is a Greek word originally meaning 'to breathe' (Stone, 1998), which came to signify life, or the animating principle (liveliness) in humans and other living beings. As a metaphor, 'soul' can also be applied to the world, and to other entities that are more or less living – institutions, groups, even professions. I am asking therefore, what is the life and soul of psychiatry or mental health care? Those who care for the very vitality of human beings should be concerned about the life and soul of the discipline, the services and the people who offer such care.

During the 19th century, the study of the mind (psychology) became a scientific endeavour, and in the process, any understanding or care for the 'soul' was overlooked, if not dismissed. The more practical concern of the 19th century was what should be done about 'the mad', those on the margins, the alienated, many of whom had been gathered up into workhouses and asylums. 'Moral treatment' (restoring confidence, strengthening the mind) in fashion before 1900 may have addressed the 'soul' (for an example, see Shorter, 1997), but this fell out of favour as the early psychiatrists (also known as alienists) began to apply scientific principles to their care.

Alan Briskin (1998), writing about soul in the workplace, surveys ancient wisdom about the soul – Greek, Hebrew, Gnostic – and finds there is something to learn from all of them. His conclusion is that:

> '...the living soul has meaning today as a metaphor for coping with the tensions and contradictions and limitations of modern life... In grappling with contradictions the soul is stirred into being. Soul resides in the tension between the apparent opposites, born from our own experience and reflection on experience. Soul is paradoxical in its essence. What kills the soul in organisations is the wish to cleave the paradox in half, to ignore one side or to ignore the tension between the two sides... To think about the whole we are obliged to hold paradox together."(ibid p 239).

This seems a useful idea to pursue.

This is rather similar to Michael Jacobs' concept of faith as the 'space between' (Jacobs, 1998).

2. Losing Soul

In the course of mental health care, we learn to recognise when a person's spirits are low (when they are depressed), when they have lost a sense of reality (in psychosis), when they change as people because of loss of memory (in dementia). Working in mental health services (and in other workplaces too) we sometimes detect that our team or our workplace is similarly altered – it may lose its sense of purpose, its direction, its morale. Or it may be that as we get to grips with what the science of mental health care is all about, we find ourselves wondering whether it has stayed in touch with the very people with whom it should be concerned. We could say that these are all instances of loss of soul.

Soul is intrinsically human, and if it dies, so does the body, the individual, the group or the institution of which it is part. When the humanity is lost from the very business of caring for 'souls' – for the aspect of people which is closest to their continuing to thrive as human beings, then there can be little hope of being really effective in this work. 'Care' is a more appropriate term than 'cure' in the realm of the soul and of mental health care, because holistic 'cure' is more than a quick fix. Care is ongoing attentiveness, and is best given by those who are as attentive to their own inner work as they are to the conflicts and character of other people.

There is a variety of reasons why mental health workers, including psychiatrists, lose 'soul'. Soul may be discerned as a sort of space where people interact with the work they do. In the workers, loss of soul may arise from their personality, their background, their beliefs and attitudes. As far as the workplace is concerned, loss of soul may be traced to its goals, assumptions and practices. Research trying to confront this has recently found that it takes more than preventive and therapeutic measures for staff – such as staff groups and counselling – to create a healthy workplace. It takes more even than a thorough look at an organisation from top to bottom, and putting a good strategy in place. It requires managers and staff working together on the problem, and doing it in a way that makes sense of their lives and of the whole context they work in (Cartwright, 1999).

A second cause of loss of soul is the effect on mental health workers of stress – a series of consequences ending in burn-out or depression. It is now widely acknowledged that this is a major issue in British workplaces of all kinds. We are gradually conceding that the causes and the effects of stress are often more subtle and far-reaching than we have dared to admit. One key effect is loss of our effectiveness in doing the job we are there to do – a symptom of loss of soul.

3. Values and Soul

A good example of addressing soul in the sense I am using it is the present concern that mental health services be local and accessible for those who use them. It was recognised that when somebody with mental health problems was admitted to a hospital perhaps as much as 50 miles away from their home, too many life-giving factors were removed from the situation; in effect, their 'soul' was virtually lost. Mental health care had swung too far the way of the institution. The result was that in the old hospitals a large group of people could be seen who had lost their vitality, their drive and their reason for living – a problem which was called 'institutional neurosis' because the asylum had become more of an issue than the problem for which its survivors were originally taken there. So a wholesale reconstruction of mental health services has been initiated to bring the vitality of everyday living in ordinary neighbourhoods back into the equation.

To do this, those planning services had to think hard about their values and the key qualities that motivated them, which often redressed the way things had been previously. It was an exercise in restoring soul. Nowadays, services aim to be local and accessible to those who use them. They also strive to be comprehensive, flexible and empowering to their clients, by focusing on strengths and skills, being racially and culturally appropriate, incorporating natural community supports and meeting special needs (Foskett, 1996).

Values like these help us to weigh up the pros and cons in a particular situation, so that we can think about practical action. Caring for human beings should not be like working through a pre-set protocol to correct a faulty machine. Each plan has to be tailor-made to an individual. The more this makes us wrestle with loose ends and uncertainty, the nearer we come to finding a good way through.

4. Soul and Psychiatry

Before psychiatry began to bring a scientific viewpoint to the relief of mental disorder, the 'care of souls' had been the concern of priests of religion, sometimes for good, sometimes not. A conflict arose between psychiatry and Christianity, not least because of the different ways each views madness. Both have spawned abuses which the other can criticise. *'Religion is psychiatry's last taboo and madness is religion's taboo'* (Foskett, 1996). But a scientific view, much as it may have advanced biological and psychological aspects of care, has by no means provided a complete solution to the needs of individuals struggling with the disorientation and suffering of disturbed mental health. It is another case of throwing out the baby with the bathwater, of a clear need for both religion *and* pscchiatry, of soul being compromised by a swing too far in one direction.

Those who know their way about both fields, religion and psychiatry, can see that careful and respectful dialogue could be most creative. It requires those on the two sides of any question to hold the tension between the possibilities of both views, without closing the debate with the insistence that one view is 'the truth'.

A major divide within psychiatry has always been between those who emphasise the biological – what are now called the neurosciences; and those who accentuate psychological and psychosocial ways of thinking. This is akin to the nature–nurture debate, the question of whether ill-health stems from heredity or the environment. For a long time, psychiatrists took the view that depression was either biological or reactive to the environment: in fact it is often both. It is now largely accepted that such arguments can be sterile, because truth lies in the way the two views interact.

In the past decade the Human Genome project (Wilkie, 1993) has given an enormous boost to our understanding of the genetic and biological aspects of being human. But if we assume that is the 'answer' to mental health problems, the soul can be obscured if not lost. It is more difficult to live with the tension between the two poles of such debates. Human solutions can never be precise. It is in this space between the two that the very soul of being human is nurtured.

In practical terms, this is expressed in the daily balancing of medication and personal support, or of medical needs and social adjustment. It is of interest that there is a fair amount of research which tends to show that counselling or psychotherapy with drug treatment can be more helpful than either on its own in the treatment of people with some forms of mental illness. The implication of this is that those responsible for the medical treatment need to work very closely with those dealing with the psychological and social issues. This is often the basis for working in teams, and so it is within the process of team work that finding the right balance, or maintaining the soul of the individual, is achieved.

5. Supporting Soul

There are times when staff in any service feel under pressure from management, and an Us-and-Them rift develops. If either side predominates, the soul of the enterprise will be damaged. Alan Briskin (1998) helpfully distinguishes the two movements present in any organisation – the preserving perspective and the purposeful perspective. The former functions as if its main purpose is to preserve existing patterns, and is focused internally on people and their feelings, their language, customs and rituals. The purposeful system is concerned with how the whole group accomplishes its objectives, and is based on relationships with the outside world, the market, the customers, the community around. Both of these perspectives cannot be observed

Looking to the Future © Pavilion Publishing/Mental Health Foundation, 2000

simultaneously, especially when we are part of the organisation concerned.

When we try to hold these two perspectives together, we discover the tensions between what is actually happening and what we would like to achieve. These tensions often show up in teams as well as in the whole organisation. It is in grappling with contradictions that soul is stirred into being. How do we hold opposing points of view and still move forward?

The well known psychiatrist and writer M. Scott Peck (1987) recognised the crucial importance of trying to discover community in whatever group we find ourselves in. It is in this process that we learn to hold the tensions between the way we really are, and the way we would like to be. When a group meets to attempt to become a community, the first stage of the process is to set some boundaries so that the group members can be safe with one another. They are initially polite, cautious, and not their total selves. As they begin to trust one another, they start to reveal who they really are. Soon they realise that they are all heading in different directions, some with great feeling, some on the sidelines. There are too many opinions for the group to move together. In fact, it feels like chaos. If they tolerate this, the group members eventually begin to let go of their prejudices and strong opinions, and naturally feel empty and vulnerable. They are more ready for community, but as yet are not going anywhere. It is only as they trust what is happening, as they learn to trust each other, as they suspend the judgements and preferences they started with, that what is good for the group as a whole can begin to emerge.

This pattern, though not taking exactly the same form, can be seen in the work of the National Association for Staff Support. For some ten years this organisation has organised residential conferences in which Health Service staff in the UK get together to see how they can support one another in their workplaces. In such a setting, a great deal has been learned about listening to the other side's point of view, holding tensions and contradictions (which abound in the Health Service!), learning to value one another and restore soul to their organisations.

It is a practice that can be commended to teams involved in community work. In effect, those who are helping others to find their place in the community need to be finding their own place in the community of their own teams if they are to survive and if they are to have any life and 'soul' to energise their clients.

6. Soul and Faith

The most obvious need for restoring soul within psychiatry is precisely where many service users are crying out for it – in the places where they encounter deep distress and pose questions about 'ultimate meanings': Who am I? What is my life, and is it worth living? What can I do with my life? Wouldn't it be better to die?

A survey of over 400 users of mental health services carried out by the Mental Health Foundation in 1996 revealed that religious or spiritual beliefs played a part in the lives of over half of those surveyed (*The Courage To Bare Our Souls*, 1999). Another survey in 1997 showed that 88% of a sample of service users reported that they had some kind of religious or spiritual belief (of users approached, 50% completed questionnaires) (*Promoting Mental Health*, 1999) Many were helped by their beliefs but a few had found certain aspects of Christian faith, churches or the people within them to be harmful. The report refers to taboos around the discussion of religious beliefs within mental health services, whereas a growing number of studies emphasise the importance of religious beliefs and the high value of support from religious communities for people with mental health problems.

It is a difficulty that mental health professionals are less religious than the average person in the population and are uncertain how best to respond to the spiritual needs of their users (Neeleman & King, 1993). The Health Education Authority report notes that religious groups (churches, synagogues and other faith communities) may recognise needs such as the search for meaning and spiritual hunger (HEA, 1999). They can spend time with people, affirming them, giving them support and help, a sense of dignity, hope, and an experience of community. They can offer guidance, counselling and pastoral visits. This sort of care can be protective against depression, can counter the impact of racism or inequalities, and can lend an understanding both of suffering and of the capacity of human beings to triumph in adversity.

Four co-ordinating chaplains have recently been appointed by Avalon NHS Trust to promote a spiritual and religious element within mental health services, and particularly to 'identify the soul within the service' (Foskett, 1999). The Avalon project is a good example of responding to the requests of service users to make a provision that the mental health service had pushed to one side because the professionals had not known how to tackle it.

But this is not a task solely for chaplains, but for every mental health worker. It is not a case of having the disposition for spiritual questions, so much as being able to extend our own awareness to the point where we can listen and respond to needs at a level deeper than the physical and problem-solving. What reviving the soul of psychiatry needs is not just doctors talking to clergy, but psychiatrists and service providers talking to service users, mental health workers talking to the churches and other places of worship, and everybody taking time to understand the difficulties faced by the families of those with mental health problems (Foskett, 1996).

7. Conclusion

This chapter has suggested a way of recognising where the soul of individuals and organisations is being lost, maintained or restored. It has concluded that holding the tension between the opposite poles of the paradoxes we confront in our everyday work is a key to the living dynamic and essential humanness of mental health work. Various examples of this process are offered. In the end, to be the connection between two live wires may demand all we have got, and drive us to seek out a personal spirituality that is equal to the challenge. There are signs that the Health Service is beginning to recognise this. In the light of the history of mental health services, it is high time to address the central issues of mental health patients, systems and theories, and of the managers and workers involved in delivering services.

References

Bhugra, D. (Ed) (1996) *Psychiatry and Religion - Context, Consensus and Controversies.* London: Routledge

Briskin, A. (1998) *The Stirring of Soul in the Workplace.* San Francisco: Berrett-Koehler.

Cartwright, S. (1999) Stress: Have Things Moved On? *Newslink,* May edition NASS, pp3–5.

Foskett, J. (1996) Christianity and Psychiatry. In: D. Bhugra (Ed) *Psychiatry and Religion.* London: Routledge

Foskett, J. (1999) Soul Searching Within the Service. *Mental Health, Religion and Culture* **2** (1) 11–17.

Health Education Authority (1999) *Promoting Mental Health - the Role of Faith Communities - Jewish and Christian Perspectives.* London: HEA.

Jacobs, M. (1998) Faith as the 'Space Between'. In: M. Cobb & V. Robshaw (Eds) *The Spiritual Challenge of Health Care.* Edinburgh: Churchill Livingstone.

Mental Health Foundation (1999) *The Courage To Bare Our Souls.* London: MHF

Neeleman, J. & King, M. B. (1993) Psychiatrists' Religious Attitudes in Relation to Their Clinical Practice. *Acta Psychiatrica Scandinavica* **88** 420–424.

Scott Peck, M. (1987) *The Different Drum.* London: Rider.

Shorter, E. (1997) *A History of Psychiatry - From the Era of the Asylum to the Age of Prozac.* New York: John Wiley & Sons.

Stone, M. (1998) *Healing the Mind - a History of Psychiatry from Antiquity to the Present.* London: Pimlico (WW Norton & Co).

Stoter, D. (1995) *Spiritual Aspects of Health Care.* London: Mosby.

Wilkie, T. (1993) *Perilous Knowledge: the Human Genome Project and its Implications.* London: Faber & Faber.

Further reading and reference

Copsey, N. (1997) *Keeping Faith - the Provision of Community Health Services Within a Multi-faith Context.* London: Sainsbury Centre for Mental Health.

Foskett, J. (1984) *Meaning in Madness.* London: SPCK.

Grainger, R. (1979) *Watching for Wings.* London: Darton, Longman & Todd.

Pattison, S. (1989) *Alive and Kicking.* London: SCM Press.

National Association for Staff Support (NASS) is an association of professionals with a common interest in co-ordinating and developing staff support resources for all health care staff. It produces its own literature, quarterly newsletter and organises conferences and workshops. Address: 9 Caradon Close, Woking, Surrey GU21 3DU Tel: 01483 771599.

Re-Defining the Code of Honour

I wrote the following poem when trying to make sense of the 'coping strategies' used by the Asian women I interviewed for the Strategies for Living project at the Mental Health Foundation.

The poem touches upon the context within which ways of coping are chosen, the circumstances surrounding the choices made when faced with dire, often painful situations. It reflects my thoughts and my own observations on the often contradictory circumstances faced by many Asian women. I was both profoundly moved – as well as inspired – by the tremendous capacity for survival against the odds. Being of Asian origin myself, I found certain aspects of my own family life being reflected back to me, and echoes of the stories relayed to me over the years from within and outside of psychiatric services: the issues faced within the family and community; the issues faced when discrimination in many guises contributes to mental distress; the further despair caused when psychiatric services fail to understand the complexities – as well as our strengths.

My poem attempts to capture the way in which all of these layers affect each other, and how cultural tradition, enshrined in deep-rooted values and judgements – about what is considered the right or wrong way of living our lives – can adversely affect mental health but can, ultimately, lead to a clearer view of what needs changing.

Dedicated to the Asian women I interviewed and to the community based organisations that helped them realise their strengths, *Re-Defining the Code of Honour* explores the concepts of *Izzat* (pride/honour) and *Sharam* (shame) which pervade many an Asian woman's sense of identity.

Mina Sassoon

Re-Defining the Code of Honour

We're strong
We cope
We struggle and survive
Against the odds
Guiding everyone's lives
We're the carers
the counsellors
the advisers
the childbearers
the homemakers
the breadwinners
the dutiful wife and daughter.
We ensure no shame befalls us
by close regard to others
pushing aside our needs.
In the name of Honour.

But what is this Honour?
And what is this shame?
When all that we do
Is riddled with blame?
When we're beaten
          ignored
                    overlooked
          and abused
When in trying to please everyone, we end up confused.
And we're told....
'You must try harder to be more demure,
to be more respectful, considerate and pure.
To keep the kids quiet, to keep the house clean.
to put up with ill-temper, put up with the scenes.'
In the name of Honour.

So back to our duties, trying harder each time,
to be how tradition defines us...
and ourselves we blame.

But when the struggle defeats us
and we cry out in pain,
we get labelled psychotic, depressed and insane.
Prescribed pills to numb us by the family GP
And we silently wonder 'is this a conspiracy?'

But if we dare voice this,
we're called paranoid.
So sink slowly, and deeper
back into the void.

We dare not take our problems outside,
for this too, is taboo.
So we silently wonder 'what are we to do?'
The institutions meant to help in times of distress
just re-enforce our alienation, just add to our stress.
They only blame our culture, tell us to escape and break out.
They just don't understand what it's all about.
For in a society where racism is rife,
yes – an oppressed man, for example, may take it out on his
wife.
But it's not that simple, so many layers to explore:
when a community exists within a climate of hostility,
oppressions within it, often rise to the fore.

But my message to you all here today is that...
Pain can, and does lead to transformation,
the openings of pathways never before considered.
When things get tough, our personal resources show
themselves.
Take stock of your achievements, no matter how small they
appear to you
Reach out to each other, we're our own best resource,
as women we're creative, together a strong force.
Explore your feelings, your desires and dreams.

   Looking to the Future © Pavilion Publishing/Mental Health Foundation, 2000

We can re-define the code of honour -
based on our needs.

Today is our day and so be all our tomorrows.
Make time for yourselves, time to play and be joyful
Explore what's available, build up a network of support
Yes – we'll still be strong and nurturing
But we'll no longer take all this blame.

Mina Sassoon, 1999

Also Available From Pavilion

A Stakeholder's Approach to Innovation in Mental Health Services

A reader for the 21st century

Edited by Professor Shulamit Ramon

This book brings together the real and varied experiences of professionals and service users, working together to develop new and imaginative services from concept to policy and practice. It looks at the need and opportunities for innovation, as well as identifying the barriers to it – physical, social, political and bureaucratic – and offers suggestions and advice on how to avoid these barriers.

This book is a must for all those working in the field of mental health looking for inspiration and practical help in challenging poor services and setting up new ones.

Format: 300pp handbook.

Product Code 60P   ISBN 1 84196 019 5

HAS 2000 Evidence-based Standards for the National Service Frameworks

Published by Pavilion Publishing and Health Advisory Service 2000

The Health Advisory Service (HAS 2000) has developed a highly effective approach for assessing systematically the quality of local services against a comprehensive framework of national standards. Following 18 months of extensive research, consultation and piloting, HAS 2000 has produced evidence-based standards that underpin its work in reviewing services. These newly developed sets of standards produced as 50-page manuals are designed to guide providers of mental health and older people services in preparing for reviews and inspections.

Standards for Mentally Disordered Offenders
Product Code 08J   ISBN 1 900600 95 1

Standards for Adult Mental Health Services
Product Code 09J   ISBN 1 900600 06 4

Standards for Mental Health Services for Older People
Product Code 10J   ISBN 1 900600 11 0

Standards for Health and Social Care Services for Older
People
Product Code 11J   ISBN 1 900600 16 1

Standards for Child and Adolescent Mental Health Services
Product Code 12J   ISBN 1 84196 024 1

Whose Reality is it Anyway?

Putting social constructionism into everyday clinical practice
– an introduction

Isabelle Ekdawi, Sue Gibbons, Elizabeth Bennett and Gillian Hughes

How we make sense of the world depends on our past experience, current context and social interactions with others. This video-accompanied training pack has been developed by a group of clinical psychologists at Newham Community NHS Trust who have developed a practice approach incorporating social constructionist philosophy.

The model explains the basis of social constructionism and provides a step-by-step guide of how this can be put into clinical practice. The resource incorporates clinical illustrations, exercises, discussion points and a clinical example to illustrate learning points.
Published by Pavilion Publishing.

Format: ringbound materials including video (35 mins) plus trainer's notes (80pp) incorporating exercises and OHP masters.

Product Code 62P   ISBN 1 84196 022 5

Teamwork

A training resource for the review and development of Mental Health Teams

Andrew Bleach

Recognising the needs of multidisciplinary teams to develop and enhance their work in the face of change, this pack emphasises the importance of each team member's contribution, showing that what each member thinks, feels and does, reflects on the team as a whole.

The training focuses on the important issues affecting mental health teams, such as the implementation of care management and the Care Programme Approach, and the multidisciplinary co-working of CPNs, social workers, psychologists and therapists.

Of special interest to: team facilitators and trainers.

Published by Pavilion Publishing in association with The Sainsbury Centre for Mental Health.

Format: ringbound materials including facilitator's notes (88pp) incorporating handouts & OHP masters.

Product code 01J   ISBN 1 900600 25 0

NVQ Booklet

By popular request we have compiled an accompanying NVQ booklet to the *Training in Mental Health* Series Parts 1, 2 and 3.

The booklet, for trainers and students, cross references all the underpinning knowledge requirements for Level 3 and Level 4 Care NVQ and Level 3 Promoting Independence NVQ with the courses in the packs.

Format: three ringbinders incorporating training resource materials (600pp in total).

Product Code 45P   ISBN 1 900600 51 X